1982

ROMANCE

ROMANCE

Modes of Literature Series

Edited by

Ashley Brown
John L. Kimmey

University of South Carolina

Charles E. Merrill Publishing Company
Columbus, Ohio
A Bell & Howell Company

Preface

The *Modes of Literature* Series differs from most anthologies introducing college students to literature by stressing synthesis as well as analysis. It organizes stories, poems, and plays into modes rather than into fiction, poetry, and drama. The purpose of this arrangement is to unify the selections in an organic and meaningful way so that they relate to each other and provide a cohesive approach to a variety of works from American, English, and Continental literatures.

We define a mode both as a mood or attitude which the writer assumes toward his subject and the form or manner in which the subject reveals itself. During the 18th Century, for instance, when satire was an important mode, a poet or prose writer searched the world around him for subjects to attack or ridicule. His mood could be bitter, his attitude ironic, his tone either facetious or angry. To express his views he might use the mock-epic, such as Alexander Pope did in *The Rape of the Lock,* or the manner of a travel book which Voltaire adopted for *Candide.*

The major modes of literature are epic, tragedy, comedy, tragicomedy, satire, and romance. All of these are represented in the five volumes of this anthology with the exception of epic. Limitations of space obviously make it impossible to reprint a long poem such as the *Aeneid.* As for the novel, we do not regard it as a separate mode, for it might be epical, tragic, comic, satiric, romantic, or a combination of these. Throughout the five volumes our emphasis is on fairly long works, although we include a number of short poems and stories. Many of these long works are familiar, part of the cultural heritage of the Western World. Their association with a mode, however, places several of them in a new light. Wordsworth's "Michael" is an example of a poem that read in terms of tragedy becomes a stronger and more complex work than it is generally thought to be. Less familiar selections such as Chekhov's "Ward No. 6," Aldous Huxley's "Nuns at Luncheon,"

Elizabeth Bishop's "The Burglar of Babylon," and Robert Lowell's *Benito Cereno* add a freshness often absent from texts that usually rely on the tried and the conventional.

There are a number of advantages to our approach. Instead of viewing a literary work as having only a tenuous connection with the one preceding or following it in an anthology, we see it as belonging to a diverse group of poems, plays, and stories that exhibit the common characteristics of one of the major modes. This mode, then, becomes the precise focus of attention. In a romance , for instance, not only does the student analyze *The Tempest* and "The Rime of the Ancient Mariner" but through them and other works he develops an understanding of what romance is, how it has evolved, who are some of its important writers, and what kinds of experience it presents in different ages. While there is much to be said for restricting the study of literature to a concern with style and form, or centering it on significant social and moral themes, either method in itself tends to be one-sided. Our approach engages the student simultaneously in a formal interpretation of literature and a consideration of the vital themes it embodies.

Although the sequence of tragedy, comedy, tragicomedy, satire, and romance is the one we recommend, the five modes can be taken up separately and in any order. Each volume is self-sufficient and does not depend on any other. Occasionally, however, there are references in the introduction or a question to another mode, but these are kept to a minimum. Their aim is to show how the modes touch and cross despite their lines of division.

The selections in this particular volume do not in any sense attempt to represent the entire history of romance.The introductory essay largely fulfills this function. Its purpose also is to suggest approaches to the poems, stories, and plays included and to stimulate the reader to arrive at his own conclusions about their romantic nature.

We wish to thank Betty Trueblood for her assistance in preparing this manuscript. Her efficiency is exceeded only by her abundant good humor. We also wish to express our gratitude to Jane Kimmey for her suggestions and her encouragement.

A. B.

J. L. K.

Contents

Introduction	I
Anonymous The Wife of Usher's Well	8
Anonymous Kemp Owyne	II
Anonymous The Demon Lover	14
Geoffrey Chaucer The Franklin's Tale	17
William Shakespeare The Tempest	41
Samuel Taylor Coleridge	
The Rime of the Ancient Mariner	112
John Keats La Belle Dame Sans Merci	135
Alfred, Lord Tennyson The Lady of Shalott	138
Alexander Pushkin The Queen of Spades	144
Edgar Allan Poe William Wilson	166
Gustave Flaubert	
The Legend of St. Julian the Hospitaller	183
Franz Kafka The Hunter Gracchus	202
Walter de la Mare The Listeners	207
Robert Frost The Witch of Coös'	209
Elizabeth Bowen The Demon Lover	214
Truman Capote The Headless Hawk	221
Biographical Notes	240

ROMANCE

Romance: Introduction

Romance is the most comprehensive of the literary modes since it includes aspects of all the others. It is the hardest to define yet the easiest to identify. This apparent contradiction stems from the word itself which today means so many vague and confusing things. We think of it in connection with love, with far-off times and places, with fiction that is at the opposite extreme from realism. Often we use it to berate whatever we find in literature to be exaggerated, sentimental, or idealistic. Particularly in a world where we pride ourselves on being tough-minded and practical we link it with fairy tales, even children's stories, that our sophisticated taste cannot accept in a serious way. However, romance, like tragedy, comedy, tragicomedy, and satire, occupies an important place in the history of literature. The stories of King Arthur as well as *Pilgrim's Progress, Gulliver's Travels, The Scarlet Letter*, and more recently Herbert Read's *The Green Child* and William Golding's *Lord of the Flies*, all belong to the tradition of romance. The heroes of these works inhabit a world which though strange and remote still reflects our human condition significantly.

The term was originally used in a very restricted sense to denote the vernacular language of France derived from Latin, hence the designation of French as a romance language. Eventually it referred to almost any book written in French. During the Middle Ages English writers most often applied the word to a work idealized in setting and elevated in language and sentiment dealing with the heroes of Troy, Britain, and King Arthur's court. Stories of these Arthurian knights and their love for beautiful, noble women in distress were especially popular, and when we think now of medieval romance, whether in verse or prose, we think of the Court of King Arthur. English and French poets celebrated him and his Round Table in such famous romances as *Sir Gawain and the Green Knight, Yvain*, and *Launce-lot*. One principal feature of these stories is the introduction of the improbable, a characteristic that has remained a part of every work one can call a romance from the Middle Ages until modern times. Another feature is the wooing of a lovely but unattainable lady by a knight. She demands that he act as her servant in his courting and that he undergo trials and suffer agonizing passions before winning her. The third basic characteristic,

1

adopted from the epic, is the hero's combat with dragons, giants, and sorcerers, as well as villainous knights. Although none of these elements except the improbable make up our fiction today, the French novel is called a *roman*, a word which suggests a work of the imagination somewhat comparable to the medieval romance.

The romantic mode continued to flourish in the Renaissance by combining with the epic, the drama, and the pastoral narrative. Edmund Spenser's *The Faerie Queen* with its elaborate allegory is the most striking example of the English romantic epic. Here once more is the long leisurely account of knights and their superhuman feats in battling monsters and villains as well as their devotion to lovely ladies in danger. Shakespeare's *The Tempest*, a play he wrote late in his career, can be classified as romantic drama because of its combination of enchantment and idyllic love. Pastoral romances in prose, such as Sir Philip Sidney's *Arcadia* set in an exotic land and featuring a complex plot complete with battles, oracles, lovers disguised as shepherds, and intrigues of every description, were popular in the late 16th Century. Their vogue extended into the 17th Century and inspired new forms of the genre. One of these forms, the sentimental romance, arose in France with the publication of Honoré d'Urfé's *Astrée*. It describes a golden age of polite shepherds and shepherdesses who spend their time discoursing on love in the most elegant and high-flown language. This type of narrative in turn was succeeded by French heroic romances that fused the noble sentiments of *Astrée* with the wild adventure common to *Arcadia*. By the end of the 17th Century, however, romance despite its popularity with the reading public no longer attracted writers in a serious way. Its place in prose fiction was gradually being taken by the realistic novel. William Congreve, the dramatist, made clear in 1692 the distinction between the two. To him romance dealt with the love and courage of heroes and heroines, used a "lofty language," and told of the "miraculous" and the "impossible." On the other hand, the novel was composed of "more familiar material" that had about it a greater verisimilitude. Romances gave the reader "more of wonder," novels "more delight."

Although romance continued to attract readers of all ages in the 18th Century, after 1700 it came under increasing attack from neo-classical critics and writers who associated it with unbridled imagination. But with the renewed interest in medieval literature as shown by Thomas Percy's collection of ballads and songs *Reliques of Ancient English Poetry* in 1765, the mode became once more firmly established. It embraced many different forms and eventually designated a whole period the Romantic Age. There were Gothic romances such as *The Castle of Otranto* (1764) by Horace Walpole and *The Monk* (1795) by Matthew G. Lewis that dramatized the supernatural with emphasis on its horrifying aspects. Next came such poems as "The Rime of the Ancient Mariner" (1798) by Coleridge that revived the medieval ballad along with its folklore and "St. Agnes Eve" (1820) by Keats that evoked the atmosphere of mysterious castles. At approximately the same time Keats was writing, Sir Walter Scott published his *Ivanhoe* (1819) to re-create the chivalric hero of the Middle Ages and his love of honor, courage, and combat. English writers of the 19th Century as varied as Dickens, Charlotte and Emily Brontë, Stevenson, and Hardy, not to mention American writers of the same period such as Hawthorne and Melville, used features of the mode in their work. Hawthorne especially wished to establish himself as a romancer. In fact, he made it a point to distinguish between his own books, which he called romances, and those of other writers, which he called novels. The difference is a significant one. A romance deals freely with its material and is not tied to fact. It stresses plot over character, symbols over concrete details, and introduces the magical and the mythological, or at least the improbable. Hawthorne thought of it as a "neutral territory" where the "real world and faery-land meet." The novel, on the other hand, is usually tied to detail, to depicting character with minute particulars, and to plausible events. As the late 19th Century American novelist Henry James suggested: "The real represents . . . the things we cannot possibly *not* know . . . The romantic stands . . . for the things . . . we *never* can directly know."

From such a brief account of the development of romance up to the 20th Century we can derive, if not a comprehensive definition of the mode, at least a means of identifying it no matter what form it may take in any age. Every romance involves improbable events that have no clear explanations. The characters are frequently symbolic of large moral, philosophical, or social abstractions. The hero is often engaged in a quest or a struggle which gives the narrative a kind of dialectical structure. He opposes a villain or he represents a good which opposes evil. The world these opposite forces occupy is full of mystery and at times resembles either the wish-fulfillment of a dream or the horror of a nightmare. Though there is often a sense of sadness from the passing of time and a sense of guilt from the committing of a dreadful act, there is not the finality of tragedy. Though there is often a feeling of pleasure in the land of make-believe or delight in a love affair or a victory, there is not the gaiety of comedy.

The selections chosen to represent romance in this anthology can be viewed in several different ways. First, there is the obvious historical sequence beginning with the ballad of the medieval period and ending with the modern short story. Such a survey reveals not only how constant the supernatural element of romance remains, for instance, from "The Wife of Usher's Well" to "The Witch of Coös," but how subtly it is combined with the realistic to give a certain plausibility to each work. The main difference concerns the degree of plausibility. Whereas the action of "The Wife of Usher's Well" cannot be fully accounted for in natural terms, the skeleton who climbs the stairs in the Frost poem can be understood to a great extent in psychological terms. This emphasis on the psychological grows more prominent in later romances as indicated by the stories of Poe and Capote included here. In fact, it takes the place of the marvelous in many cases. Darkness is explained as a state of mind rather than a time for souls to rise from the dead.

Then, too, there is the rewriting of older stories in terms of the writer's own age. Compare the two versions of "The Demon Lover." "La Belle Dame Sans Merci" treats almost the same theme found in the medieval ballad "Thomas Rymer." "The Lady of Shalott" derives from the Arthurian stories of the 12th and 13th Centuries and draws on much the same material as "The Franklin's Tale." "St. Julian" stems from the medieval genre known as the saint's legend as does to an extent "The Hunter Gracchus." "The Headless Hawk" uses the device known as the "double" so evident in "The Queen of Spades" and "William Wilson" and common to much 19th Century fiction.*

Secondly, one can view the selections here from the standpoint of types. The ballad, a story in song form, is of two kinds, the folk ballad and the literary ballad. The anonymous ballad has certain well-marked characteristics: objectivity of detail and simplicity of language, repetition of words and phrases (especially in a refrain), and the four-line ballad stanza.** A single crucial episode is presented for the most part in dramatic form with the use of dialogue and little personal commentary. Literary ballads such as "The Rime of the Ancient Mariner" and "La Belle Dame Sans Merci" are more complex in structure and language as well as more subjective in the treatment of theme and character. They employ a greater variety of imagery and metrical patterns. While they do suggest the dramatic form in their development of plot, it is not common. Although "The Lady of Shalott" and "The Listeners" are narrative poems and "The Witch of Coös" is dramatic verse, they resemble the folk ballad in their objective rendering of scenes, in

---

* The term "double" refers to the shadowy or opposite self of the hero, terrifyingly real only to him. Associated with primitive superstitions and myths and common in the dream and vision literature of earlier times, it became a frequent device during the Romantic Age when the imagination was given free reign. Robert Lewis Stevenson's *Dr. Jekyll and Mr. Hyde* and Dostoevsky's short novel *The Double* helped to popularize it in the 19th Century. Modern writers on psychology such as Jung, Freud, and Otto Rank have related it to man's unconscious, his irrational nature, and the body-soul duality. Novelists as different as Conrad (*The Secret Sharer*), Thomas Mann (*Doctor Faustus*), and Vladimir Nabokov (*Pale Fire*) have used it in their work.

** The four-line ballad stanza consists of lines rhyming *abcb* with the first and second lines having four accents and the second and fourth three accents. Folk ballads are sung. Literary ballads are not meant to be sung.

their repetition of words and phrases, and in their concentration on a single theme or episode. They resemble the literary ballad in their intricate verse forms and their subjective depiction of character.

"The Franklin's Tale," called a Breton lay (a short narrative poem set in Brittany and dealing mainly with chivalric love), is in essence a medieval romance. It features the doctrine of courtly love in which a squire woos a married woman according to a prescribed ritual. In addition to the love interest that is standard in every medieval romance, there are also elements of the supernatural. These link it on one hand to the ballad and on the other hand to the Gothic romance of the late 18th Century. Such tales at first featured haunted castles and ghosts in clanking armor, but later focused on a multiplicity of horror devices from underground passageways to monsters such as the one found in *Frankenstein*. "The Queen of Spades," "William Wilson," Elizabeth Bowen's "The Demon Lover," and "The Headless Hawk" are full-fledged Gothic stories with their atmosphere of terror and mystery.

By contrast "St. Julian" and "The Hunter Gracchus" are didactic tales that resemble, as noted above, the medieval saint's legend. The action is relatively simple and straightforward. There is no analysis of the characters, no attempt to see them from within. Traditional religious symbolism and allegory control both the depiction of character and the development of plot, and the emphasis is placed on suffering and martyrdom.

Third, one can examine these selections from the standpoint of their main themes. The most obvious and dramatic one is that of revenge. It is found in the two versions of the demon lover legend where the devil makes a woman who is untrue to him pay for her betrayal. It is also found in *The Tempest*, where the dispossessed duke of Milan seeks vengeance against his usurping brother only to forgive him in the end. Closely allied to this primitive motif is the theme of retribution and penance found in "The Rime of the Ancient Mariner" and "St. Julian." Here the hero's killing of God's creatures results in his suffering and his longing for expiation. Interestingly enough, "The Witch of Coös" suggests this same pattern to an extent: a crime, a period of suffering, and a search for a way to unburden the soul. The mother and son after living for years with their guilty secret finally reveal it to a stranger in somewhat the same fashion the Ancient Mariner does to the Wedding Guest, though without his obsessiveness. The idea of a man haunted by his other self or demon dominates "William Wilson" and "The Headless Hawk." Both stories end significantly with the narcissistic image of the mirror and with a sense of endless pain and frustration. Another theme suggested in "The Headless Hawk," the loss of faith, or spiritual impotence, forms the conclusion of "The Hunter Gracchus." And still another motif of the Capote story, the isolation of the hero who had "sub-

stituted for a sense of reality a knowledge of time and place," runs through
"The Lady of Shalott" where the heroine is described as living in an unreal
realm of shadows. She, too, looks at herself and the world outside her in a
self-imprisoning mirror.

Of course enchantment and love are also main themes in many of these
poems and stories. "The Wife of Usher's Well" centers on the miraculous
return from death of a woman's sons and her devotion to them as if they
were alive. "Kemp Owyne" combines the same two motifs of magic and love
as do "La Belle Dame Sans Merci," the two versions of "The Demon Lover,"
and "The Franklin's Tale." In the latter the dilemma of the thoughtless wife,
who promises herself to a courtly lover in return for his removing the rocks
in the sea which endanger her husband's journey home, almost turns a
romance into a tragedy. But the sanctity of marriage triumphs over the threat
of adultery, and true devotion is restored and false enchantment banished.
The two lovers in *The Tempest*, though belonging to opposing families, are
united. Not so happy is the ending of many romances where the familiar
note of melancholy is sounded. The sons in "The Wife of Usher's Well" say
goodbye to their mother forever at the crowing of the cock. The woman in
the ballad "The Demon Lover" sinks into the sea. The knight in "La Belle
Dame Sans Merci" is left in a land where no birds sing. The hero of "The
Queen of Spades" goes mad. Idyllic as many romances appear to be, the
writer is always aware of the real dangers within the imaginary gardens.

Last, one can view the selections from the standpoint of their structure,
which involves a quest in the form of a mysterious search or journey. The
action is of two kinds. The majority of the works included here move from
the initial scene of anticipation to the moment of satisfaction to the inevitable disillusionment. Such a pattern occurs in "The Wife of Usher's
Well," the two versions of "The Demon Lover," "The Rime of the Ancient
Mariner," "La Belle Dame Sans Merci," "The Lady of Shalott," "The
Queen of Spades," "William Wilson," "The Hunter Gracchus," and "The
Headless Hawk." The movement in the other works is from the introductory
problem to the irreconcilable conflict to the unexpected happy solution.
Such a pattern occurs in "Kemp Owyne," "The Franklin's Tale," *The Tempest*, and "St. Julian." Within these broad outlines are of course many intricate designs. The point is that a romance, though often more loosely orga-
nized than a tragedy, comedy, or satire, nevertheless does have a form that is
discernible, meaningful, and in many respects peculiar to the mode because
of the nature of the subject. It is not superimposed on the story but grows out
of the material.

Such is the variety as well as the unity of the mode. If romance does not
seem at first to reflect our anxiety-ridden age as fully as tragedy, comedy,
tragicomedy, or satire, on closer examination we can see that its exploita-

tion of the irrational is at the heart of much modern literature. In fact, it is this method that many writers today rely on to interpret the bewildering and frightening phenomena of our world.

Suggestions for Further Reading

Chase, Richard. *The American Novel and Its Tradition.* New York: Doubleday and Company, Inc., 1957.

Eigner, Edwin M. *Robert Lewis Stevenson and Romantic Tradition.* Princeton: Princeton University Press, 1966.

Frye, Northrop. *The Anatomy of Criticism.* Princeton: Princeton University Press, 1957.

Frye, Prosser Hall. *Romance and Tragedy.* Boston: Marshall Jones Co., 1922.

Gerould, Gordon Hall. *The Ballad Tradition.* Oxford: The Carendon Press, 1932.

Jackson, W. T. H. *The Literature of the Middle Ages.* New York: Columbia University Press, 1960.

Johnston, Arthur. *Enchanted Ground: The Study of Medieval Romance in the Eighteenth Century.* London: The Athlone Press, 1964.

Ker, W. P. *Epic and Romance.* London: Macmillan and Co., 1908.

Shakespeare, William. *The Tempest,* ed. by Frank Kermode. London: Methuen and Co., 1958.

Stevenson, Lionel. *The English Novel.* Boston: Houghton Mifflin Company, 1960.

Weston, Jessie L. *From Ritual to Romance.* New York: Peter Smith, 1941.

Anonymous

The Wife of Usher's Well

There lived a wife at Usher's Well,
And a wealthy wife was she;
She had three stout and stalwart sons,
And sent them o'er the sea.

They hadna been a week from her,
A week but barely ane,
When word came to the carline[1] wife
That her three sons were gane.

They hadna been a week from her,
A week but barely three,   10
When word came to the carline wife
That her sons she'd never see.

"I wish the wind may never cease,
Nor fashes[2] in the flood,
Till my three sons come hame to me
In earthly flesh and blood!"

It fell about the Martinmas,[3]
When nights are lang and mirk,[4]
The carline wife's three sons came hame,
And their hats were o' the birk.[5]   20

---

[1] Old.
[2] Troubles.
[3] Feast of St. Martin, Nov. 11.
[4] Dark.
[5] Birch.

It neither grew in syke[6] nor ditch,
Nor yet in ony sheugh;[7]
But at the gates o' Paradise
That birk grew fair eneugh.

"Blow up the fire, my maidens!
Bring water from the well!
For a' my house shall feast this night,
Since my three sons are well."

And she has made to them a bed,
She's made it large and wide;   30
And she's ta'en her mantle her about,
Sat down at the bedside.

Up then crew the red, red cock,
And up and crew the gray;
The eldest to the youngest said,
" 'Tis time we were away."

The cock he hadna crawed but once,
And clapped his wings at a',[8]
When the youngest to the eldest said,
"Brother, we must awa'."   40

"The cock doth craw, the day doth daw,
The channerin'[9] worm doth chide;
Gin we be missed out o' our place,
A sair pain we maun bide."[10]

"Lie still, lie still but a little wee while,
Lie still but if we may;
Gin my mother should miss us when she wakes,
She'll go mad ere it be day."

---

6 Field.
7 Furrow.
8 At all. Crowing of the cock signals that the dead must return to their graves.
9 Fretting.
10 A sour pain we must endure.

"Fare ye weel, my mother dear!
Fareweel to barn and byre![11]   50
And fare ye weel, the bonny lass
That kindles my mother's fire."

Questions for Discussion

1. What are the elements of romance in the ballad?

2. How is the return of the three sons made to seem natural and inevitable?

3. How are the mother's world and the sons' world contrasted?

4. Give examples of understatement and explain their effectiveness in terms of presenting the ironies of the situation.

5. What do you think is the significance of the reference to the "bonny lass" in the last stanza?

---

[11] Cattle barn.

Anonymous

Kemp Owyne

Her mother died when she was young,
    Which gave her cause to make great moan;
Her father married the warst woman
    That ever lived in Christendom.

She served her with foot and hand,
    In every thing that she could dee,
Till once, in an unlucky time,
    She threw her in ower Craigy's sea.

Says, "Lie you there, dove Isabel,
    And all my sorrows lie with thee;   10
Till Kemp Owyne come ower the sea,
    And borrow you with kisses three,
Let all the world do what they will,
    Oh borrowed shall you never be!"

Her breath grew strang, her hair grew lang,
    And twisted thrice about the tree,
And all the people, far and near,
    Thought that a savage beast was she.

These news did come to Kemp Owyne,
    Where he lived, far beyond the sea;   20
He hasted him to Craigy's sea,
    And on the savage beast looked he.

Her breath was strang, her hair was lang,
    And twisted was about the tree,
And with a swing she came about:
    "Come to Craigy's sea, and kiss with me.

11

"Here is a royal belt," she cried,
  "That I have found in the green sea;
And while your body it is on,
  Drawn shall your blood never be;   30
But if you touch me, tail or fin,
  I vow my belt your death shall be."

He stepped in, gave her a kiss,
  The royal belt he brought him wi;
Her breath was strang, her hair was lang,
  And twisted twice about the tree,
And with a swing she came about:
  "Come to Craigy's sea, and kiss with me.

"Here is a royal ring," she said,
  "That I have found in the green sea;   40
And while your finger it is on,
  Drawn shall your blood never be;
But if you touch me, tail or fin,
  I swear my ring your death shall be."

He stepped in, gave her a kiss,
  The royal ring he brought him wi;
Her breath was strang, her hair was lang,
  And twisted ance about the tree,
And with a swing she came about:
  "Come to Craigy's sea, and kiss with me.   50

"Here is a royal brand," she said,
  "That I have found in the green sea;
And while your body it is on,
  Drawn shall your blood never be;
But if you touch me, tail or fin,
  I swear my brand your death shall be."

He stepped in, gave her a kiss,
  The royal brand he brought him wi;
Her breath was sweet, her hair grew short,
  And twisted nane about the tree,   60
And smilingly she came about,
  As fair a woman as fair could be.

Questions for Discussion

1. Why are there only two stanzas of introduction before the main action of the ballad? Are they at all written, do you think, with the last stanza in mind?

2. Kemp Owyne is a knight of King Arthur's court. To what extent does this account, do you think, for his being mentioned by the stepmother and his hastening to "Craigy's Sea"?

3. Why do you think the breath and hair are singled out to indicate Isabel's repulsiveness?

4. Does the absence of dialogue in the ballad lessen its dramatic effectiveness? Why does Kemp Owyne never speak?

5. Does the ballad illustrate the powers of enchantment, of love, of chivalry, three common features of romance? Or some other aspect of romance?

Anonymous

The Demon Lover

"O where have you been, my long, long love,
    This long seven years and mair?"
"O I'm come to seek my former vows
    Ye granted me before."

"O hold your tongue of your former vows,
    For they will breed and strife;
O hold your tongue of your former vows,
    For I am become a wife."

He turned him right and round about,
    And the tear blinded his ee: 10
"I wad never hae trodden on Irish ground,
    If it had not been for thee.

"I might hae had a king's daughter,
    Far, far beyond the sea;
I might have had a king's daughter,
    Had it not been for love o thee."

"If ye might have had a king's daughter,
    Yer sel ye had to blame;
Ye might have taken the king's daughter,
    For ye kend[1] that I was nane.   20

"If I was to leave my husband dear,
    And my two babes also,
O what have you to take me to,
    If with you I should go?"

---

[1] Knew.

"I hae seven ships upon the sea—
  The eighth brought me to land—
With four-and-twenty bold mariners,
  And music on every hand."

She has taken up her two little babes,
  Kissd them baith cheek and chin: 30
"O fair ye weel, my ain two babes,
  For I'll never see you again."

She set her foot upon the ship,
  No mariners could she behold;
But the sails were o the taffetie,
  And the masts o the beaten gold.

She had not sailed a league, a league,
  A league but barely three,
When dismal grew his countenance,
  And drumlie² grew his ee.   40

They had not sailed a league, a league,
  A league but barely three,
Until she espied his cloven foot,
  And she wept right bitterlie.

"O hold your tongue of your weeping," says he,
  "Of your weeping now let me be;
I will shew you how the lilies grow
  On the banks of Italy."

"O what hills are yon, yon pleasant hills,
  That the sun shines sweetly on?"   50
"O yon are the hills of heaven," he said,
  "Where you will never win."³

"O whaten a mountain is yon," she said,
  "All so dreary wi frost and snow?"

---

² Gloomy.
³ Gain, get to.

"O yon is the mountain of hell," he cried,
  "Where you and I will go."

He strack the tap-mast wi his hand,
  The fore-mast wi his knee,
And he brake that gallant ship in twain,
  And sank her in the sea.   60

Questions for Discussion

1. Although a supernatural figure, what human characteristics does the Demon Lover possess? Are these presented through exaggeration or understatement? Explain.

2. Why does the wife leave her family for her lover so readily? Does she experience any conflict? Is she attracted by promises of wealth or by the irresistible power of the Demon Lover?

3. Divide the ballad into scenes. Where is the climax? How is it prepared for? What device makes it particularly effective?

4. Why does the Demon Lover show his former love heaven before he shows her hell?

5. Despite its fantastic happenings is the ballad more credible than "The Wife of Usher's Well" and "Kemp Owyne"? If not, why not?

Geoffrey Chaucer (ca. 1343–1400)

The Franklin's Tale

From *The Canterbury Tales*

TRANSLATED BY NEVILL COGHILL

In Brittany, or as it then was called,
Armorica, there was a knight enthralled
To love, who served his lady with his best
In many a toilsome enterprise and quest,
Suffering much for her ere she was won.
   She was among the loveliest under sun
And came from kindred of so high a kind
He scarce had the temerity of mind
To tell her of his longing and distress.
But in the end she saw his worthiness   10
And felt such pity for the pains he suffered,
Especially for the meek obedience offered,
That privately she fell into accord
And took him for her husband and her lord
—The lordship husbands have upon their wives.
And to enhance the bliss of both their lives
He freely gave his promise as a knight
That he would never darken her delight
By exercising his authority
Against her will or showing jealousy,   20
But would obey in all with simple trust
As any lover of a lady must;
Save this his sovereignty in name upon her
He should preserve, lest it should shame his honour.
   She thanked him, and with great humility
Replied, 'Sir, since you show a courtesy

"The Franklin's Tale" by Geoffrey Chaucer, from *the Canterbury Tales*, translated by Nevill Coghill. Reprinted by permission of John Farquharson Ltd.

So fair in proffering me so free a rein,
God grant there never be betwixt us twain,
Through any fault of mine, dispute or strife.
Sir, I will be your true and humble wife,   30
Accept my truth of heart, or break, my breast!'
Thus were they both in quiet and at rest.

    For there's one thing, my lords, it's safe to say;
Lovers must each be ready to obey
The other, if they would long keep company.
Love will not be constrained by mastery;
When mastery comes the god of love anon
Stretches his wings and farewell! he is gone.
Love is a thing as any spirit free;
Women by nature long for liberty   40
And not to be constrained or made a thrall,
And so do men, if I may speak for all.

    Whoever's the most patient under love
Has the advantage and will rise above
The other; patience is a conquering virtue.
The learned say that, if it not desert you,
It vanquishes what force can never reach;
Why answer back at every angry speech?
No, learn forbearance or, I'll tell you what,
You will be taught it, whether you will or not.   50
No one alive—it needs no arguing—
But sometimes says or does a wrongful thing;
Rage, sickness, influence of some malign
Star-constellation, temper, woe or wine
Spur us to wrongful words or make us trip.
One should not seek revenge for every slip,
And temperance from the times must take her schooling
In those that are to learn the art of ruling.

    And so this wise and honourable knight
Promised forbearance to her that he might   60
Live the more easily, and she, as kind,
Promised there never would be fault to find
In her. Thus in this humble, wise accord
She took a servant when she took a lord,
A lord in marriage in a love renewed
By service, lordship set in servitude;
In servitude? Why no, but far above
Since he had both his lady and his love,

His lady certainly, his wife no less,
To which the law of love will answer 'yes.'   70
   So in the happiness that they had planned
He took his wife home to his native land
With joyful ease and reached his castle there
By Penmarch Point, not far from Finisterre,
And there they lived in amity unharried.
   Who can recount, unless he has been married,
The ease, the prosperous joys of man and wife?
A year or more they lived their blissful life
Until it chanced the knight that I have thus
Described and who was called Arveragus   80
Of Caer-rhud, planned to spend a year or so
In Britain (no, not Brittany), to go
And seek high deeds of arms and reputation
In honour; that was all his inclination.
He stayed two years, at least the book says thus.
   Now I will pause about Arveragus
And turn to speak of Dorigen his wife
Who loved her husband as her own heart's life.
   She wept his absence, sighed for him and pined
As noble wives will do when so inclined;   90
She mourned, lay wakeful, fasted and lamented,
Strained by a passion that could be contented
Only by him, and set the world at naught.
Her friends who knew the burden of her thought
Brought her such consolations as they might;
They preached to her, they told her day and night,
'You'll kill yourself for nothing.' Such relief
And comfort as is possible to grief
They fuss about to find, and finding, press
Upon her to relieve her heaviness.   100
   Slow is the process, it is widely known,
By which a carver carves his thought in stone,
Yet cuts at last the figure he intended;
And slowly too, thus soothed and thus befriended,
Her soul received the print of consolation
Through hope and reason, and her long prostration
Turned to recovery, she ceased to languish;
She couldn't be always suffering such anguish.
   Besides Arveragus as it befell
Sent letters to her saying all was well   110

And that he shortly would be home again;
Only for that her heart had died of pain.

Her friends, seeing her grief began to ease,
Begged her for heaven's sake and on their knees
To come and roam about with them and play
And drive her darker fantasies away,
And finally she granted their request
And clearly saw it would be for the best.

Her husband's castle fronted on the sea
And she would often walk in company   120
High on the ramparts, wandering at large.
Many a ship she saw and many a barge
Sailing such courses as they chose to go;
But these made part and parcel of her woe
And she would often say, 'Alas for me,
Is there no ship, so many as I see,
To bring me home my lord? For then my heart
Would find a cure to soothe its bitter smart.'

At other times she used to sit and think
With eyes cast downward to the water's brink   130
And then her heart endured a thousand shocks
To see such jagged, black and grisly rocks,
So that she scarce could stand upon her feet.
Then she would refuge in some green retreat,
Lie on a lawn, and looking out to sea
With long, cold sighs, would murmur piteously:

'Eternal God that by thy providence
Guidest the world in wise omnipotence,
They say of Thee that Thou hast nothing made
In vain; but, Lord, these fiendish rocks are laid   140
In what would rather seem a foul confusion
Of work than the creation and conclusion
Of One so perfect, God the wise and stable;
Why madest Thou thy work unreasonable?
These rocks can foster neither man nor beast
Nor bird, to north or south, to west or east;
They are a menace, useless, to my mind.
Lord, seest Thou not how they destroy mankind?
A hundred thousand bodies dead and rotten
Have met their death on them, though now forgotten;   150
Thy fairest work, wrecked on a rocky shelf,
Mankind, made in the image of Thyself.

It seemed that then Thou hadst great charity
Towards mankind; how therefore may it be
That Thou hast fashioned means as these to harm them
That do no good, but injure and alarm them?
   'I know it pleases scholars to protest
In argument that all is for the best,
Though what their reasons are I do not know.
   'But O Thou God that madest wind to blow,   160
Preserve my husband, that is my petition!
I leave the learned to their disquisition.
But would to God these rocks so black, so grim,
Were sunk in Hell itself for sake of him!
They are enough to kill my heart with fear.'
Thus she would speak with many a piteous tear.
   Her friends could see it gave her no relief
To roam the shore, but added to her grief,
And so they sought amusement somewhere else.
They led her by the water-ways and wells   170
And many another scene of loveliness;
They danced, they played backgammon, they played chess.
   And so one sunny morning, as they'd planned,
They went into a garden near at hand
Where they had staged a picnic and supplied
Victuals enough and other things beside,
And there they lingered out the happy day.
   It was the morning of the sixth of May
And May had painted with her softest showers
A gardenful of leafiness and flowers;   180
The hand of man with such a cunning craft
Had decked this garden out in pleach and graft.
There never was a garden of such price
Unless indeed it were in Paradise.
The scent of flowers and the freshening sight
Would surely have made any heart feel light
That ever was born, save under the duress
Of sickness or a very deep distress;
Pleasure and beauty met in every glance.
   And after dinner they began to dance   190
And there was singing; Dorigen alone
Made her continual complaint and moan
For never among the dancers came to view
Her husband, he that was her lover too.

Nevertheless she had to pass the day
In hope and let her sorrows slide away.
 Now in this dance, among the other men,
There danced a squire before Dorigen,
Fresher and jollier in his array,
In my opinion, than the month of May.   200
He sang and danced better than any man
There is or has been since the world began.
He was, what's more, if I could but contrive
To picture him, the handsomest man alive,
Young, strong and wealthy, mettlesome, discreet,
And popular as any you could meet;
And shortly, if I am to tell the truth,
All unbeknown to Dorigen, this youth
—A lusty squire and servant in the game
Of Venus, and Aurelius was his name—   210
Had loved her best of any for two years
And longer so it chanced, but still his fears
Had never let him bring the matter up;
He drank his draught of penance without cup.[1]
 He had despaired of her and dared not say
More of his passion than he might convey
In general terms, by saying that he burned
With love but that his love was not returned;
On all such themes he fashioned many a phrase,
Wrote songs, complaints, roundels and virelays   220
Saying his griefs were more than he dared tell,
He languished as a fury did in Hell,
And he must die, he said, as Echo did
For young Narcissus and the love she hid.[2]
But in no other way, as said above,
Had he the courage to confess his love,
Save that perhaps from time to time at dances,
Where youth pays love's observances, his glances
It well may be would linger on her face
Beseechingly, as is the common case;   230
But she was unaware of what he meant.

---

[1] He drank misery from the cask and not in small draughts.

[2] Echo, because she offended Hera, wife of Zeus, was condemned to have the last word but no power to utter the first. Hence she was frustrated in her love for Narcissus, who rejected her advances. She wasted away in the mountains until nothing was left of her but her voice.

Nevertheless it happened, ere they went
Out of the garden, since he lived nearby
And was of good position, standing high
In honour and had known her from of old,
They fell in speech and he at last grew bold
And drew towards the purpose in his head.
Taking his opportunity he said:
   'Madam, by God's green earth and all its treasure,
Had I imagined it could give you pleasure   240
That day, on which your lord Arveragus
Went over sea, then I, Aurelius
Would have gone too, and never come again.
I know the service of my love is vain,
My recompense is but a bursting heart.
   'Madam, have pity on the pain and smart
Of love; a word from you can slay or save.
Would God your little feet stood on my grave!
There is no time to say what I would say;
Have mercy, sweetheart, chase me not away.'   250
   She looked at him with closer scrutiny
And answered, 'Are you saying this to me?
Can you intend it? Never,' she said, 'till now
Had I suspected that—what you avow.
But by the Lord that gave me soul and life
I never mean to prove a faithless wife
In word or deed if I can compass it.
I will be his to whom I have been knit.
Take that for final answer, as for me.'
   But after that she added playfully,   260
'And yet, Aurelius, by the Lord above
I might perhaps vouchsafe to be your love,
Since I perceive you groan so piteously.
Look; on the day the coasts of Brittany
Are stone by stone cleared of these hateful rocks
By you, so that no ship or vessel docks
In danger, when, I say, you clear the coast
So clean there's not a single stone to boast,
I'll love you more than any man on earth;
Accept my word in truth for all it's worth.'   270
   'Is there no other way than this?' said he.
   'No, by the Lord,' she said, 'that fashioned me.
For it will never happen, that I know;

So clear your heart of fancies, let them go.
How can a man find daintiness in life
Who goes about to love another's wife,
That can enjoy her body when he pleases?'
    Aurelius sighed again. The long uneases
Of lovers' woe returned on hearing this
And he replied with sorrowing emphasis,   280
'Madam, it is impossible to do,
So I must die a horrible death, for you.'
And on the word he turned and went away.
    Her other many friends came up to play
And wander with her through the leafy walk
Of alleys pleached, but of her lover's talk
They did not know. Revels began anew,
On till the dazzling sun had lost its hue
For the horizon reft it of its light;
This is as much to say that it was night.   290
So they went home delighted, all in joy
Except, alas, Aurelius, wretched boy.
    He sought his house, a sigh at every breath,
And could see no way of avoiding death.
Within himself he felt his heart turn cold
And falling on his knees began to hold
His hands to heaven and the upper air
In raving madness, and he said a prayer.
Excessive suffering had turned his head,
He knew not what he spoke, but this he said,   300
With pleading heart and pitiful, to one
And all the gods, beginning with the sun:
    'Apollo, God and Governor, whose power
Tends over every plant and herb and flower
And tree, appointing unto each by reason
Of thy celestial course, his time and season,
According as thy arc is low or high,
Lord Phoebus, in thy mercy cast an eye
On sad Aurelius, wretched and forlorn.
Look on me, Lord! My lady-love has sworn   310
To prove my death, though for no fault in me,
Unless, O Lord, in thy benignity
Thou pity a dying heart; for well I know,
Shouldest thou please, Lord Phoebus, to bestow
Thy mercy, thou canst help me best of all

Except my lady; listen to my call,
Vouchsafe to hear me, Lord, if I expound
A means of help and how it may be found.
   'Thy blissful sister, Luna the Serene,
Chief goddess of the ocean and its queen,   320
Though Neptune have therein his deity,
Is over him and empress of the sea.
Thou knowest, Lord, that just as her desire
Is to be lit and quickened by thy fire,
For busily she follows after thee,
Just so the natural longing of the sea
Follows on her and so is bound to do;
She is its goddess and the rivers' too.
   'And so, Lord Phoebus, this is my request,
Do me this miracle—or burst, my breast!—   330
That even now at thy next opposition
Which is to be in *Leo*, thou petition
Thy sister to bring floods so much increased
That they shall rise five fathom at the least
Above the highest rock that now appears
In Brittany, and let this last two years.
Then to my lady I can safely say,
"Keep truth with me, the rocks are all away."
   'Lord Phoebus, do this miracle for me now!
Beg her to go no faster, Lord, than thou;   340
I say, beseech thy sister that she go
No faster than thyself two years or so,
Then she will stay at full, and at their height
The spring floods will continue, day and night.
And should she not vouchsafe in such a way
The granting of my lady, then I pray
That she may sink the rocks, that they be drowned
Within her own dark region underground
Where Pluto dwells, for while they are above
I cannot hope to win my lady-love.   350
   'Barefoot to Delphi will I go and seek
Thy temple! See the tears upon my cheek,
Lord Phoebus, have compassion, grant my boon!'
And on the word he fell into a swoon
And long he lay upon the ground in trance.
   His brother who had heard of his mischance
Found him and caught him up, and off to bed

He carried him. With torment in his head
I leave this woeful creature, if to die
In desperation he must chose, not I.   360
    Meanwhile Arveragus in health and power
Came honourably home, the very flower
Of chivalry, with other noble men.
How art thou blissful now, my Dorigen!
Thou hast a lusty husband to thy charms,
Thine own fresh knight, thy honoured man-at-arms
That loves thee as his life, in whom there springs
No inclination to imagine things
Or ask if anyone while he was out
Has talked to thee of love. But not a doubt   370
Entered his head; he had no thought in life
Except to dance and joust and cheer his wife
In blissful joy; and so I leave him thus
And turn again to sick Aurelius.
    In furious torment, languishing away,
Two years and more wretched Aurelius lay
Scarce with the strength to put his foot to ground.
No comfort during all that time he found
Save in his brother, who was a learned man
And privy to his grief since it began,   380
For to no other could Aurelius dare
Ever to say a word of his affair.
More secretly he guarded his idea
Than ever did Pamphilus for Galatea.[3]
To all appearances his breast was whole,
But a keen arrow stuck within his soul.
A wound that's only surface-healed can be
A perilous thing, you know, in surgery,
Unless the arrow-head be taken out.
    His brother wept for him and fell in doubt   390
Of his recovery until by chance
It came to him that when he was in France
At Orleans—he was a student then—
He lusted in his heart like all young men
To study things prohibited, to read
In curious arts of magic, and indeed

---

[3] Pamphilus and Galatea are the lovers in the medieval Latin love poem *Pamphilus de Amore.*

Search every hole and corner with defiance
To learn the nature of that special science.
And he remembered how he took a look
One morning, in his study, at a book   400
On natural magic which it chanced he saw
Because a friend, then bachelor-at-law
Though destined later to another trade,
Had hidden it in his desk. This book displayed
The workings of the moon; there were expansions
In detail on the eight-and-twenty mansions
Belonging to her—nonsense such as that,
For nowadays it isn't worth a gnat,
Since holy church has managed to retrieve us
And suffers no illusions now to grieve us.   410

   And so, remembering this book by chance
His heart as suddenly began to dance
For joy within him; suddenly reassured,
He said, 'My brother shall be quickly cured
For I am certain that there must be sciences
By which illusions can be made, appliances
Such as these subtle jugglers use in play
At banquets. Very often, people say,
These conjurors can bring into a large
And lofty hall fresh water and a barge   420
And there they seem to row it up and down;
Sometimes a lion, grim and tawny-brown,
Sometimes a meadow full of flowery shapes,
Sometimes a vine with white and purple grapes,
Sometimes a castle which by some device,
Though stone and lime, will vanish in a trice,
Or seem at least to vanish, out of sight.

   'So I conclude that if I only might
Discover some old fellow of the kind
Who has these moony mansions in his mind   430
At Orleans, or has some power above
All this, my brother might enjoy his love.
A learned man could hoodwink all beholders
With the allusion that the rocks and boulders
Of Brittany had vanished one and all
And ships along the brink could safely call,
Coming and going, and if it but endured
A day or two my brother could be cured.

She will be forced to recognize his claim
Or else she will at least be put to shame.'   440
    Why draw my story out? What need be said?
He went to where his brother lay in bed
And brought him so much comfort with his plot
To visit Orleans, that up he got
And started off at once upon the road
High in the hope of lightening his load.
    They neared the city; when it seemed to be
About two furlongs off, or maybe three,
They met a youngish scholar all alone
Who greeted them in Latin, in a tone   450
Of friendly welcome and he struck them dumb
In wonder with 'I know why you have come.'
And ere they went a step upon their way
He told them all they had in mind to say.
    The Breton scholar wanted to be told
About the friends that they had known of old
And he replied that they were all now dead;
He spoke with feeling, many tears were shed.
    Down from his horse Aurelius soon alighted
To follow the magician, who invited   460
Him and his brother home, set them at ease
And served them victuals; nothing that could please
Was lacking and Aurelius soon decided
He'd never seen a house so well provided.
    And the magician caused there to appear
Before their supper, parks of forest deer
And he saw stags among them, antlered high,
The greatest ever seen by human eye.
He saw a hundred of them killed by hounds
And others, arrow-wounded, lay in mounds.   470
Next, when the deer had vanished, he was shown
A river bank and there a hawk was flown
By falconers; they saw a heron slain.
    Then he saw knights at joust upon a plain
And after that Aurelius was entranced
At seeing his beloved as she danced
And he, it seemed, was dancing with her too.
And when the master of this magic view
Saw it was time he clapped his hands and banished
The figures, and farewell! our revels vanished.   480

Yet all the time they had not left the house
While being shown these sights so marvellous,
But sat within his study where there lay
His books about them; there were none but they.
    The master called the squire who was to set
Their meal, and said, 'Is supper ready yet?
It's very near an hour I could swear,'
He added, 'since I told you to prepare,
When these two gentlemen came in with me
To see my study and my library.'   490
    'Sir,' said the squire, 'it's ready, and you may
Begin, if it so please you, right away.'
'Then let us eat,' he said; 'that will be best;
These amorous people sometimes need a rest.'
    After they'd eaten bargaining began;
What payment should this master-artisan
Have to remove the rocks of Brittany
From the Gironde to where the Seine meets sea?
He made it difficult and roundly swore
He'd take a thousand pounds for it or more,   500
He wasn't too eager even at that price.
Aurelius with his heart in paradise
Readily answered, 'Fie on a thousand pound!
I'd give the world, which people say is round,
The whole wide world, if it belonged to me;
Call it a bargain then, for I agree.
You shall be truly paid it, on my oath.
But look, be sure no negligence or sloth
Delay us here beyond to-morrow, now!'
The scholar gave him answer 'That I vow.'   510
    Aurelius went to bed in high delight
And rested soundly pretty well all night.
Tired by his journey and with hope retrieved
He slept, the troubles of his heart relieved.
    And morning came; as soon as it was day
They made for Brittany by the nearest way,
The brothers with the wizard at their side,
And there dismounted having done their ride.
It was—so say the books, if I remember—
The cold and frosty season of December.   520
Phoebus grew old, his coppered face was duller
Than it had been in *Cancer* when his colour

Shone with the burnished gold of streaming morn,
But now descending into *Capricorn*
His face was very pale, I dare maintain.
The bitter frosts, the driving sleet and rain
Had killed the gardens; greens had disappeared.
Now Janus[4] by the fire with double beard,
His bugle-horn in hand, sits drinking wine;
Before him stands a brawn of tusky swine,   530
And '*Sing Noël!*' cries every lusty man.

　　Aurelius, using all the means he can,
Gives welcome to the master, shows respect
And begs his diligence, that no neglect
Or sloth delay the healing of his smart,
Lest he should kill himself, plunge sword in heart.

　　This subtle sage had pity on the man
And night and day went forward with his plan
Watching the hour to favour the conclusion
Of his experiment, that by illusion   540
Or apparition—call it jugglery,
I lack the jargon of astrology—
She and the world at large might think and say
The rocks had all been spirited away
From Brittany or sunk under the ground.

　　And so at last the favouring hour was found
To do his tricks and wretched exhibition
Of that abominable superstition.
His calculating tables were brought out
Newly corrected (he made sure about   550
The years in series and the single years
To fix the points the planets in their spheres
Were due to reach and so assessed their 'root'
In longitude) and other things to suit,
Such as his astrolabe,[5] and argument
From arc and angle, and was provident
Of fit proportionals for the minor motion
Of planets, and he studied with devotion,
Measuring from the point where Alnath[6] swam

---

　　[4] Two-headed god after which January was named. He knew both the past and the future.

　　[5] Astronomical instrument for taking the altitude of the sun or stars and finding the solution of other astronomical problems.

　　[6] The star Arietis.

In the eighth sphere, to where the head of the *Ram*   560
Stood in the ninth, in its eternal station
(As we suppose), and made his calculation.
And finding the first mansion of the moon,
He calculated all the rest in tune
With that. He worked proportionally, knowing
How she would rise and whither she was going
Relative to which planets and their place,
Equal or not, upon the zodiac face.
And thus according to his calculations
He knew the moon in all her operations   570
And all the relevant arithmetic
For his illusion, for the wretched trick
He meant to play, as in those heathen days
People would do. There were no more delays
And by his magic for a week or more
It seemed the rocks were gone; he'd cleared the shore.
   Aurelius, still despairing of the plot,
Nor knowing whether he'd get his love or not,
Waited for miracles by night and day
And when he saw the rocks were cleared away,   580
All obstacles removed, the plot complete,
He fell in rapture at his master's feet.
'Wretch as I am, for what has passed between us,
To you, my lord, and to my lady Venus
I offer thanks,' he said, 'for by your care,
As poor Aurelius is well aware,
He has been rescued from a long dismay.'
   And to the temple then he took his way
Where, as he knew, his lady was to be;
And when he saw his opportunity   590
With terror in his heart, and humbled face,
He made obeisance to her sovereign grace.
   'My truest lady,' said this woeful man,
'Whom most I dread and love—as best I can—
Last in the world of those I would displease,
Had I not suffered many miseries
For love of you, so many I repeat
That I am like to perish at your feet,
I would not dare approach you, or go on
To tell you how forlorn and woebegone   600
I am for you; but I must speak or die.

You kill me with your torture; guiltless, I.
Yet if my death could never so have stirred
Your pity, think before you break your word.
Repent, relent, remember God above you
Before you murder me because I love you.
You know what you have promised to requite
—Not that I challenge anything of right,
My sovereign lady, only of your grace—
Yet in a garden yonder, at such a place   610
You made a promise which you know must stand
And gave your plighted truth into my hand
To love me best, you said, as God above
Knows, though I be unworthy of your love.
It is your honour, madam, I am seeking;
It's not to save my life that I am speaking.
I have performed what you commanded me
As if you deign to look you soon will see.
Do as you please but think of what you said
For you will find me here alive, or dead.   620
It lies in you to save me or to slay—
But well I know the rocks are all away!'
He took his leave of her and left the place.
　　Without a drop of colour in her face
She stood as thunderstruck by her mishap.
'Alas,' she said, 'to fall in such a trap!
I never had thought the possibility
Of such a monstrous miracle could be,
It goes against the processes of nature.'
And home she went, a very sorrowful creature   630
In deadly fear, and she had much to do
Even to walk. She wept a day or two,
Wailing and swooning, pitiful to see,
But why she did so not a word said she,
For her Arveragus was out of town.
But to herself she spoke and flinging down
In pitiable pallor on her bed
She voiced her lamentation and she said:
　　'Alas, of thee, O Fortune, I complain,
That unawares hast wrapped me in thy chain,   640
Which to escape two ways alone disclose
Themselves, death or dishonour, one of those,
And I must choose between them as a wife.

Yet I would rather render up my life
Than to be faithless or endure a shame
Upon my body or to lose my name.
My death will quit me of a foolish vow;
And has not many a noble wife ere now
And many a virgin slain herself to win
Her body from pollution and from sin?   650
  'Yes, surely, many a story we may trust
Bears witness; thirty tyrants full of lust
Slew Phido the Athenian[7] like a beast,
Then had his daughters carried to their feast,
And they were brought before them in despite
Stark naked, to fulfil their foul delight,
And there they made them dance upon the floor,
God send them sorrow, in their father's gore.
And these unhappy maidens, full of dread,
Rather than they be robbed of maidenhead,   660
Broke from their guard and leapt into a well
And there were drowned, so ancient authors tell.
  'The people of Messina also sought
Some fifty maidens out of Sparta, brought
Only that they might work their lechery
Upon them, but in all that company
Not one that was not slain; they were content
To suffer death rather than to consent
To being forced in their virginity;
What then's the fear of death, I say, to me?   670
  'Consider Aristoclides for this,
A tyrant lusting after Stymphalis
Who, when her father had been slain one night,
Fled for protection to Diana's might
Into her temple, clung to her effigy
With both her hands and from it could not be
Dragged off, they could not tear her hands away
Till they had killed her. If a virgin may
Be seen to have so loath an appetite
To be defiled by filthy man's delight,   680
Surely a wife should kill herself ere she
Were so defiled, or so it seems to me.
  'And what of Hasdrubal? Had he not a wife

---

[7] The following stories are from St. Jerome's antifeminist work *Against Jovinian*.

At Carthage who had rather take her life?
For as she watched the Romans win the town
She took her children with her and leapt down
Into the fire; there she chose to burn
Rather than let them do their evil turn.

   'Did not Lucrece choose death for her escape
In Rome of old when she had suffered rape   690
For Tarquin's lust? Did not she think it shame
To live a life that had been robbed of name?

   'The seven virgins of Miletus too
Took their own lives—were they not bound to do?—
Lest they be ravished by their Gaulish foes.
More than a thousand stories I suppose
Touching this theme were easy now to tell.

   'Did not his wife, when Abradates fell,
Take her own life and let the purple flood
Glide from her veins to mingle with his blood,   700
Saying, "My body shall at least not be
Defiled by man, so far as lies in me"?

   'Since there are found so many, if one delves,
That gladly have preferred to kill themselves
Rather than be defiled, need more be sought
For my example? Better were the thought
To kill myself at once than suffer thus.
I will be faithful to Arveragus
Or slay myself as these examples bid,
As the dear daughter of Demotion did   710
Who chose to die rather than be defiled.

   'O Skedasus, thou also hadst a child
That slew herself, and sad it is to read
How she preferred her death to such a deed.

   'As pitiable or even more, I say,
The Theban maid who gave her life away
To foil Nichanor and a like disgrace.

   'Another virgin at that very place
Raped by a Macedonian, it is said,
Died to repay her loss of maidenhead.   720

   'What shall I say of Niceratus' wife
Who being thus dishonoured took her life?

   'And O how true to Alcibiades
His lover was! She died no less than these
For seeking to give burial to her dead.

'See what a wife Alcestis was,' she said,
'And what says Homer of Penelope?
All Greece can celebrate her chastity.
   'Laodamia, robbed of all her joy,
Protesilaus being killed at Troy,   730
Would live no longer, seeing that he was slain.
   'Of noble Portia let me think again;
She could not live on being forced to part
From Brutus whom she loved with all her heart.
   'And Artemisia, faithful to her man,
Is honoured, even by the barbarian.
   'O Teuta, queen! Thy wifely chastity
Should be a mirror for all wives to see;
I say the same of Bilia and as soon
Of chaste Valeria and Rhodogoun.'   740
   Thus for a day or two she spent her breath,
Poor Dorigen, and ever purposed death.
   On the third day, however, of her plight,
Home came Arveragus, that excellent knight,
And questioned her; what was she crying for?
But she continued weeping all the more.
'Alas,' she said, 'that ever I was born!
'Thus have I said,' she answered,' thus have sworn—'
She told him all as you have heard before.
It need not be repeated here once more.   750
   Her husband smiled at her with friendly eyes
And countenance, and answered in this wise:
'And is there nothing, Dorigen, but this?'
'No, no, so help me God!' with emphasis
She answered. 'Is it not enough, too much?'
'Well, wife,' he said, 'it's better not to touch
A sleeping dog, so I have often heard;
All may be well, but you must keep your word,
For, as may God be merciful to me,
I rather would be stabbed than live to see   760
You fail in truth. The very love I bear you
Bids you keep truth, in that it cannot spare you;
Truth is the highest thing in a man's keeping.'
And on the word he suddenly burst out weeping
And said, 'But I forbid on pain of death,
As long as you shall live or draw your breath,
That you should ever speak of this affair

To living soul; and what I have to bear
I'll bear as best I may; now wash your face,
Be cheerful. None must guess at this disgrace.'   770
    He called a maidservant and squire then
And said, 'Go out with Lady Dorigen;
Attend upon her, whither she will say.'
They took their leave of him and went their way
Not knowing why their mistress was to go.
It was his settled purpose none should know.
    Perhaps a heap of you will want to say,
'Lewd, foolish man to act in such a way,
Putting his wife into such jeopardy!'
Listen before you judge them, wait and see.   780
She may have better fortune, gentlemen,
Than you imagine; keep your judgements then
Till you have heard my story which now turns
To amorous Aurelius as he burns
For Dorigen; they happened soon to meet
Right in the town, in the most crowded street
Which she was bound to use, however loath,
To reach the garden and to keep her oath.
    Aurelius gardenwards was going too;
A faithful spy on all she used to do,   790
He kept close watch whenever she went out
And so by accident or luck no doubt
They met each other; he, his features glowing,
Saluted her and asked where she was going,
And she replied as one half driven mad,
'Why, to the garden, as my husband bade
To keep my plighted word, alas, alas!'
    Aurelius, stunned at what had come to pass,
Felt a great surge of pity that arose
At sight of Dorigen in all her woes   800
And for Arveragus the noble knight
That bade her keep her word of honour white,
So loth he was that she should break her truth.
And such a rush of pity filled the youth
That he was moved to think the better course
Was to forgo his passion than to force
An act on her of such a churlish kind,
And against such nobility of mind,
So, in few words, the lad addressed her thus:

'Madam, say to your lord Arveragus   810
That since I well perceive his nobleness
Towards yourself, and also your distress,
Knowing the shame that he would rather take
(And that were pity) than that you should break
Your plighted word, I'd rather suffer too
Than seek to come between his love and you.
     'So, Madam, I release into your hand
All bonds or deeds of covenant that stand
Between us, and suppose all treaties torn
You may have made with me since you were born.   820
I give my word never to chide or grieve you
For any promise given, and so I leave you,
Madam, the very best and truest wife
That ever yet I knew in all my life.
Let women keep their promises to men,
Or at the least remember Dorigen.
A squire can do a generous thing with grace
As well as can a knight, in any case.'
     And she went down and thanked him on her knees.
Home to her husband then with heart of ease   830
She went and told him all as I've recorded.
You may be sure he felt so well rewarded
No words of mine could possibly express
His feelings. Why then linger? You may guess.
     Arveragus and Dorigen his wife
In sovereign happiness pursued their life,
No discord in their love was ever seen,
He cherished her as though she were a queen,
And she stayed true as she had been before;
Of these two lovers you will get no more.   840
     Aurelius, all whose labour has been lost,
Cursing his birth, reflected on the cost.
'Alas,' he said, 'alas that I am bound
To pay in solid gold a thousand pound
To that philosopher. What shall I do?
All I can see is that I'm ruined too.
There's my inheritance; that I'll have to sell
And be a beggar. Then there's this as well;
I can't stay here a shame and a disgrace
To all my family; I must leave the place.   850
And yet he might prove lenient; I could pay

A yearly sum upon a certain day
And thank him gratefully, I can but try.
But I will keep my truth, I will not lie.'
   And sad at heart he went to search his coffer
And gathered up what gold he had to offer
His master, some five hundred pound I guess,
And begged him as a gentleman, no less,
To grant him time enough to pay the rest.
   'Sir, I can boast, in making this request,'   860
He said, 'I've never failed my word as yet,
And I will certainly repay this debt
I owe you, master, ill as I may fare,
Yes, though I turn to begging and go bare.
If you'd vouchsafe me, on security,
A little respite, say two years or three,
All would be fine. If not I'll have to sell
My patrimony; there's no more to tell.'
   Then this philosopher in sober pride,
Having considered what he'd said, replied,   870
'Did I not keep my covenant with you?'
'You did indeed,' he said, 'and truly too.'
'And did you not enjoy your lady then?'
'No . . . no . . .' he sighed, and thought of Dorigen.
'What was the reason? Tell me if you can.'
   Reluctantly Aurelius then began
To tell the story you have heard before,
There is no need to tell it you once more.
He said: 'Her husband, in his nobleness,
Would have preferred to die in his distress   880
Rather than that his wife should break her word.'
He told him of her grief and what occurred,
How loth she was to be a wicked wife
And how she would have rather lost her life;
'Her vow was made in innocent confusion,
She'd never heard of magical illusion.
So great a sense of pity rose in me,
I sent her back as freely then as he
Had sent her to me, let her go away.
That's the whole story, there's no more to say.'   890
   Then the magician answered, 'My dear brother,
Each of you did as nobly as the other.
You are a squire, sir, and he a knight,

But God forbid in all His blissful might
That men of learning should not come as near
To nobleness as any, never fear.
  'Sir, I release you of your thousand pound
No less than if you'd crept out of the ground
Just now, and never had had to do with me.
I will not take a penny, sir, in fee   900
For all my knowledge and my work to rid
The coast of rocks; I'm paid for what I did,
Well paid, and that's enough. Farewell, good-day!'
He mounted on his horse and rode away.
  My lords, I'll put a question; tell me true,
Which seemed the finest gentleman to you?
Ere we ride onwards tell me, anyone!
I have no more to say, my tale is done.

Questions for Discussion

1. What is the attitude of Dorigen and Arveragus toward their marriage? In what way do their individual attitudes foreshadow how they react toward each other later on in the tale?

2. What leads Dorigen to think of the rocks as evil and to wish them removed? Are they truly symbols of evil in the world? Is the desire of both Dorigen and Aurelius to see them removed "a sign of weakness, of unwillingness to accept the real world," as one critic has noted?

3. Does Dorigen intend her promise to Aurelius to be taken seriously? To what extent might it be said that such a promise is more terrible than the rocks she wishes removed?

4. Contrast Aurelius' attitude toward love with that of Arveragus. To what extent does this contrast involve a conflict between courtly love and married love?

5. Why might the magician at Orleans be said to be "the most subtly interesting person of the tale"? In what way does the whole tale depend on him, his magic as well as his charity?

6. How is Dorigen's choice between death and dishonor similar to her earlier dilemma referred to in Question 3?

7. Is Arveragus' decision to have Dorigen keep her promise ridiculous, or is it the result of his belief (as one critic has noted) that "an ideal has no relevance unless we are willing to sacrifice our whole world to it"?

8. Is the husband-wife relationship of Arveragus and Dorigen at all different at the end from what it is at the beginning of the tale?

9. Is the tale a romance mainly because of the love theme, the magic motif, the happy ending, or a combination of these?

10. To what extent are the romantic aspects of this tale similar to those of the ballads you have read? To what extent are they different?

William Shakespeare (1564-1616)

The Tempest

CHARACTERS

ALONSO, King of Naples
SEBASTIAN, his brother
PROSPERO, the right Duke of Milan
ANTONIO, his brother, the usurping Duke of Milan
FERDINAND, son to the King of Naples
GONZALO, an honest old councillor
ADRIAN AND FRANCISCO, lords
CALIBAN, a savage and deformed slave
TRINCULO, a jester
STEPHANO, a drunken butler
MASTER OF A SHIP
BOATSWAIN
MARINERS
MIRANDA, daughter to Prospero
ARIEL, an airy spirit
IRIS
CERES
JUNO } presented by spirits
NYMPHS
REAPERS
OTHER SPIRITS ATTENDING ON PROSPERO

THE SCENE

An uninhabited Island

The Tempest by William Shakespeare, edited by Northrop Frye. Reprinted by permission of Penguin Books Inc.

ACT I

SCENE 1

A tempestuous noise of thunder and lightning heard. Enter a
SHIPMASTER *and a* BOATSWAIN.

MASTER. Boatswain!

BOATSWAIN. Here, master. What cheer?

MASTER. Good, speak to th' mariners; fall to't yarely, or we run ourselves aground. Bestir, bestir!   *Exit.*

Enter MARINERS.

BOATSWAIN. Heigh, my hearts! Cheerly, cheerly, my hearts! Yare,
yare! Take in the topsail! Tend to th' master's whistle! Blow till
thou burst thy wind, if room enough!

Enter ALONSO, SEBASTIAN, ANTONIO, FERDINAND, GONZALO, *and others.*

ALONSO. Good boatswain, have care. Where's the master? Play the
men.

BOATSWAIN. I pray now, keep below.   10

ANTONIO. Where is the master, bos'n?

BOATSWAIN. Do you not hear him? You mar our labor. Keep your
cabins: you do assist the storm.

GONZALO. Nay, good, be patient.

BOATSWAIN. When the sea is. Hence! What cares these roarers for
the name of king? To cabin! Silence! Trouble us not!

GONZALO. Good, yet remember whom thou hast aboard.

BOATSWAIN. None that I more love than yourself. You are a councillor: if you can command these elements to silence and work the
peace of the present, we will not hand a rope more; use your   20

---

3. *yarely,* briskly
6. *Tend,* attend
6–7. *Blow . . . wind,* (addressed to the storm)
7. *if room enough,* i.e., so long as we have sea-room
8. *Play,* (perhaps 'ply,' keep the men busy)
15. *roarers,* (1) waves (2) blusterers or bullies
20. *hand,* handle

authority. If you cannot, give thanks you have lived so long, and make yourself ready in your cabin for the mischance of the hour, if it so hap.—Cheerly, good hearts!—Out of our way, I say. *Exit.*

GONZALO. I have great comfort from this fellow: methinks he hath no drowning mark upon him; his complexion is perfect gallows. Stand fast, good Fate, to his hanging! Make the rope of his destiny our cable, for our own doth little advantage. If he be not born to be hanged, our case is miserable. *Exeunt.*

Enter BOATSWAIN.

BOATSWAIN. Down with the topmast! Yare! Lower, lower! Bring her to try with main-course! (*A cry within.*) A plague upon this howl- 30
ing! They are louder than the weather or our office.

Enter SEBASTIAN, ANTONIO, *and* GONZALO.

Yet again? What do you here? Shall we give o'er and drown? Have you a mind to sink?

SEBASTIAN. A pox o' your throat, you bawling, blasphemous, inchar-itable dog!

BOATSWAIN. Work you, then.

ANTONIO. Hang, cur, hang, you whoreson, insolent noisemaker! We are less afraid to be drowned than thou art.

GONZALO. I'll warrant him for drowning, though the ship were no stronger than a nutshell and as leaky as an unstanched wench. 40

BOATSWAIN. Lay her ahold, ahold! Set her two courses! Off to sea again! Lay her off!

Enter MARINERS *wet.*

MARINERS. All lost! To prayers, to prayers! All lost! (*Exeunt.*)

BOATSWAIN. What, must our mouths be cold?

---

25. *complexion,* indication of character in appearance of face; *gallows,* (alluding to the proverb 'He that's born to be hanged need fear no drowning')

27. *doth little advantage,* doesn't help us much

30. *try with main-course,* lie hove-to with only the mainsail; *plague,* (followed by a dash in F; possibly the boatswain's language was more profane than the text indicates; cf. l. 34, and V, i, 218–19)

31. *our office,* (the noise we make at) our work

39. *warrant . . . for,* guarantee . . . against

40. *unstanched,* i.e., loose

41. *ahold,* (perhaps 'a-hull,' without any sail. As the ship drifts to the rocks, the order is reversed and the 'two courses,' foresail and mainsail, are set up again in an effort to clear the shore.)

GONZALO. The King and Prince at prayers! Let's assist them,
  For our case is as theirs.
SEBASTIAN.   I am out of patience.
ANTONIO. We are merely cheated of our lives by drunkards. This
  wide-chopped rascal—would thou mightst lie drowning
  The washing of ten tides!
GONZALO.   He'll be hanged yet,
  Though every drop of water swear against it   50
  And gape at wid'st to glut him.
    A confused noise within: 'Mercy on us!—
    We split, we split!—Farewell, my wife and children!—Farewell,
    brother!—We split, we split, we split!'   (*Exit Boatswain.*)
ANTONIO. Let's all sink with th'King.
SEBASTIAN.   Let's take leave of him.
                                        Exit (*with Antonio*).
GONZALO. Now would I give a thousand furlongs of sea for an acre of
  barren ground—long heath, brown furze, anything. The wills
  above be done, but I would fain die a dry death.   *Exit.*

SCENE 2

Enter PROSPERO *and* MIRANDA.

MIRANDA. If by your art, my dearest father, you have
  Put the wild waters in this roar, allay them.
  The sky, it seems, would pour down stinking pitch
  But that the sea, mounting to th' welkin's cheek,
  Dashes the fire out. O, I have sufferèd
  With those that I saw suffer! a brave vessel
  (Who had no doubt some noble creature in her)
  Dashed all to pieces! O, the cry did knock
  Against my very heart! Poor souls, they perished!
  Had I been any god of power, I would   10

---

47. *merely*, completely
48. *wide-chopped*, wide-jawed
49. *ten tides*, (pirates were hanged on shore and left until three tides washed over them)
51. *glut*, gobble
57. *long heath, brown furze*, heather and gorse (sometimes emended to 'ling, heath, broom, furze')
4. *cheek*, face (with perhaps a secondary meaning of 'side of a grate')
6. *brave*, fine, handsome (and so elsewhere throughout the play)

Have sunk the sea within the earth or ere
It should the good ship so have swallowed and
The fraughting souls within her.
PROSPERO.   Be collected.
No more amazement. Tell your piteous heart
There's no harm done.
MIRANDA.   O, woe the day!
PROSPERO.   No harm.
I have done nothing but in care of thee,
Of thee my dear one, thee my daughter, who
Art ignorant of what thou art, naught knowing
Of whence I am; nor that I am more better
Than Prospero, master of a full poor cell,   20
And thy no greater father.
MIRANDA.   More to know
Did never meddle with my thoughts.
PROSPERO.   'Tis time
I should inform thee farther. Lend thy hand
And pluck my magic garment from me. So,
Lie there, my art. Wipe thou thine eyes; have comfort.
The direful spectacle of the wrack, which touched
The very virtue of compassion in thee,
I have with such provision in mine art
So safely orderèd that there is no soul—
No, not so much perdition as an hair   30
Betid to any creature in the vessel
Which thou heard'st cry, which thou saw'st sink. Sit down;
For thou must now know farther.
MIRANDA.   You have often
Begun to tell me what I am; but stopped
And left me to a bootless inquisition,
Concluding, 'Stay: not yet.'
PROSPERO.   The hour's now come:
The very minute bids thee ope thine ear.

---

11. *or ere*, before
13. *fraughting*, forming the cargo; *collected*, composed
14. *amazement*, distraction; *piteous*, pitying
22. *meddle*, mingle
25. *art*, i.e., his robe
27. *virtue*, essence
28. *provision*, foresight
30. *perdition*, loss
31. *Betid*, happened
35. *bootless inquisition*, fruitless inquiry

Obey, and be attentive. Canst thou remember
A time before we came unto this cell?
I do not think thou canst, for then thou wast not   40
Out three years old.
MIRANDA.   Certainly, sir, I can.
PROSPERO. By what? By any other house or person?
  Of any thing the image tell me that
  Hath kept with thy remembrance.
MIRANDA.   'Tis far off,
  And rather like a dream than an assurance
  That my remembrance warrants. Had I not
  Four or five women once that tended me?
PROSPERO. Thou hadst, and more, Miranda. But how is it
  That this lives in thy mind? What seest thou else
  In the dark backward and abysm of time?   50
  If thou rememb'rest aught ere thou cam'st here,
  How thou cam'st here thou mayst.
MIRANDA.   But that I do not.
PROSPERO. Twelve year since, Miranda, twelve year since,
  Thy father was the Duke of Milan and
  A prince of power.
MIRANDA.   Sir, are not you my father?
PROSPERO. Thy mother was a piece of virtue, and
  She said thou wast my daughter; and thy father
  Was Duke of Milan; and his only heir
  A princess—no worse issuèd.
MIRANDA.   O the heavens!
  What foul play had we that we came from thence?   60
  Or blessèd was't we did?
PROSPERO.   Both, both, my girl!
  By foul play, as thou say'st, were we heaved thence,
  But blessedly holp hither.
MIRANDA.   O, my heart bleeds
  To think o' th' teen that I have turned you to,

---

38. *Obey*, listen
41. *Out*, fully
43. *tell me*, i.e., describe for me
46. *remembrance warrants*, memory guarantees
50. *backward*, past; *abysm*, abyss
56. *piece*, masterpiece
59. *no worse issuèd*, no meaner in descent
63. *blessedly holp*, providentially helped
64. *teen*, trouble; *turned you to*, put you in mind of

Which is from my remembrance! Please you, father.
PROSPERO. My brother and thy uncle, called Antonio—
　I pray thee mark me—that a brother should
　Be so perfidious!—he whom next thyself
　Of all the world I loved, and to him put
　The manage of my state, as at that time　　　　　　70
　Through all the signories it was the first
　And Prospero the prime duke, being so reputed
　In dignity, and for the liberal arts
　Without a parallel; those being all my study,
　The government I cast upon my brother
　And to my state grew stranger, being transported
　And rapt in secret studies. Thy false uncle—
　Dost thou attend me?
MIRANDA.　　　　　　Sir, most heedfully.
PROSPERO. Being once perfected how to grant suits,
　How to deny them, who t' advance, and who　　　80
　To trash for over-topping, new-created
　The creatures that were mine, I say, or changed 'em.
　Or else new-formed 'em; having both the key
　Of officer and office, set all hearts i' th' state
　To what tune pleased his ear, that now he was
　The ivy which had hid my princely trunk
　And sucked my verdure out on't. Thou attend'st not?
MIRANDA. O, good sir, I do.
PROSPERO.　　　　　I pray thee mark me.
　I thus neglecting worldly ends, all dedicated
　To closeness, and the bettering of my mind　　　90
　With that which, but by being so retired,
　O'er-prized all popular rate, in my false brother
　Awaked an evil nature, and my trust,
　Like a good parent, did beget of him
　A falsehood in its contrary as great

---

65. *from*, out of
69–70. *put . . . state*, entrusted the control of my administration
71. *signories*, states of northern Italy
79. *perfected*, grown skillful
81. *trash for over-topping*, (1) check, as hounds, for going too fast (2) cut branches, as of over-tall trees
82. *or*, either
83. *key*, (used with pun on its musical sense, leading to the metaphor of 'tune')
90. *closeness*, seclusion(?) or secret studies(?)
92. *O'er-prized*, outvalued; *rate*, estimation
94. *good parent*, (alluding to the same proverb cited by Miranda in 1. 119)

As my trust was, which had indeed no limit,
A confidence sans bound. He being thus lorded,
Not only with what my revenue yielded
But what my power might else exact, like one
Who having unto truth, by telling of it,   100
Made such a sinner of his memory
To credit his own lie, he did believe
He was indeed the Duke, out o' th' substitution
And executing th' outward face of royalty
With all prerogative. Hence his ambition growing—
Dost thou hear?
MIRANDA.   Your tale, sir, would cure deafness.
PROSPERO. To have no screen between this part he played
And him he played it for, he needs will be
Absolute Milan. Me (poor man) my library
Was dukedom large enough. Of temporal royalties   110
He thinks me now incapable; confederates
(So dry he was for sway) with th' King of Naples
To give him annual tribute, do him homage,
Subject his coronet to his crown, and bend
The dukedom yet unbowed (alas, poor Milan!)
To most ignoble stooping.
MIRANDA.   O the heavens!
PROSPERO. Mark his condition, and th' event; then tell me
If this might be a brother.
MIRANDA.   I should sin
To think but nobly of my grandmother.
Good wombs have borne bad sons.
PROSPERO.   Now the condition.   120
This King of Naples, being an enemy
To me inveterate, hearkens my brother's suit;
Which was, that he, in lieu o' th' premises

97–99. *He . . . exact,* (the sense is that Antonio had the prerogatives as well as the income of the Duke)
97. *sans bound,* unlimited
98. *revenue,* (accent second syllable)
100. *unto,* (F reads 'into') ; *it,* i.e., the lie
102. *To,* as to
103. *out,* as a result
109. *Absolute Milan,* Duke of Milan in fact
111. *confederates,* joins in league with
112. *dry,* thirsty, eager
117. *condition,* pact; *event,* outcome
123. *in lieu o' th' premises,* in return for the guarantees

Of homage and I know not how much tribute,
Should presently extirpate me and mine
Out of the dukedom and confer fair Milan,
With all the honors, on my brother. Whereon,
A treacherous army levied, one midnight
Fated to th' purpose, did Antonio open
The gates of Milan; and, i' th' dead of darkness, 130
The ministers for th' purpose hurrièd thence
Me and thy crying self.
MIRANDA.   Alack, for pity!
I, not rememb'ring how I cried out then,
Will cry it o'er again; it is a hint
That wrings mine eyes to't.
PROSPERO.   Hear a little further,
And then I'll bring thee to the present business
Which now's upon's; without the which this story
Were most impertinent.
MIRANDA.   Wherefore did they not
That hour destroy us?
PROSPERO.   Well demanded, wench.
My tale provokes that question. Dear, they durst not, 140
So dear the love my people bore me; nor set
A mark so bloody on the business; but
With colors fairer painted their foul ends.
In few, they hurried us aboard a bark,
Bore us some leagues to sea; where they prepared
A rotten carcass of a butt, not rigged,
Nor tackle, sail, nor mast; the very rats
Instinctively have quit it. There they hoist us,
To cry to th' sea that roared to us; to sigh
To th' winds, whose pity, sighing back again, 150
Did us but loving wrong.
MIRANDA.   Alack, what trouble
Was I then to you!
PROSPERO.   O, a cherubin

---

125. *presently*, immediately; *extirpate*, remove (accent second syllable)
129. *Fated*, devoted
131. *ministers*, agents
134. *hint*, occasion
135. *wrings*, constrains
138. *impertinent*, irrelevant
144. *few*, few words
146. *butt*, tub

Thou wast that did preserve me! Thou didst smile,
Infusèd with a fortitude from heaven,
When I have decked the sea with drops full salt,
Under my burden groaned; which raised in me
An undergoing stomach, to bear up
Against what should ensue.
MIRANDA.   How came we ashore?
PROSPERO. By providence divine.
    Some food we had, and some fresh water, that   160
    A noble Neapolitan, Gonzalo,
    Out of his charity, who being then appointed
    Master of this design, did give us, with
    Rich garments, linens, stuffs, and necessaries
    Which since have steaded much. So, of his gentleness,
    Knowing I loved my books, he furnished me
    From mine own library with volumes that
    I prize above my dukedom.
MIRANDA.   Would I might
    But ever see that man!
PROSPERO.   Now I arise.
    Sit still, and hear the last of our sea-sorrow.   170
    Here in this island we arrived; and here
    Have I, thy schoolmaster, made thee more profit
    Than other princess can, that have more time
    For vainer hours, and tutors not so careful.
MIRANDA. Heavens thank you for't! And now I pray you, sir,—
    For still 'tis beating in my mind,—your reason
    For raising this sea-storm?
PROSPERO.   Know thus far forth.
    By accident most strange, bountiful Fortune
    (Now my dear lady) hath mine enemies
    Brought to this shore; and by my prescience   180
    I find my zenith doth depend upon
    A most auspicious star, whose influence
    If now I court not, but omit, my fortunes
    Will ever after droop. Here cease more questions.

---

157. *undergoing stomach,* resolution to endure
165. *steaded,* been of use
172. *more profit,* profit more
173. *princess,* princesses
181. *zenith,* apex of fortune
183. *omit,* neglect

Thou art inclined to sleep. 'Tis a good dulness,
And give it way. I know thou canst not choose.   (*Miranda sleeps.*)
Come away, servant, come! I am ready now.
Approach, my Ariel: come!

Enter ARIEL.

ARIEL. All hail, great master! Grave sir, hail! I come
To answer thy best pleasure; be't to fly,   190
To swim, to dive into the fire, to ride
On the curled clouds. To thy strong bidding task
Ariel and all his quality.
PROSPERO.   Hast thou, spirit,
Performed to point the tempest that I bade thee?
ARIEL. To every article.
I boarded the King's ship: now on the beak,
Now in the waist, the deck, in every cabin,
I flamed amazement: sometime I'ld divide
And burn in many places; on the topmast,
The yards, and boresprit would I flame distinctly,   200
Then meet and join. Jove's lightnings, the precursors
O' th' dreadful thunderclaps, more momentary
And sight-outrunning were not. The fire and cracks
Of sulphurous roaring the most mighty Neptune
Seem to besiege and make his bold waves tremble;
Yea, his dread trident shake.
PROSPERO.   My brave spirit!
Who was so firm, so constant, that this coil
Would not infect his reason?
ARIEL.   Not a soul
But felt a fever of the mad and played
Some tricks of desperation. All but mariners   210
Plunged in the foaming brine and quit the vessel;

---

187. *Come away*, come here
192. *task*, (supply 'come')
193. *quality*, cohorts (Ariel is leader of a band of elemental spirits)
194. *to point*, in detail
196. *beak*, prow
197. *waist*, middle; *deck*, poop
198. *flamed amazement*, struck terror by appearing as (St. Elmo's) fire
200. *boresprit*, bowsprit; *distinctly*, in different places
207. *coil*, uproar
209. *of the mad*, such as madman have

Then all afire with me the King's son Ferdinand,
With hair up-staring (then like reeds, not hair),
Was the first man that leapt; cried 'Hell is empty,
And all the devils are here!'

PROSPERO.   Why, that's my spirit!
But was not this nigh shore?

ARIEL.   Close by, my master.

PROSPERO. But are they, Ariel, safe?

ARIEL.   Not a hair perished.
On their sustaining garments not a blemish,
But fresher than before; and as thou bad'st me,
In troops I have dispersed them 'bout the isle.   220
The King's son have I landed by himself,
Whom I left cooling of the air with sighs
In an odd angle of the isle, and sitting,
His arms in this sad knot.

PROSPERO.   Of the King's ship
The mariners say how thou hast disposed,
And all the rest o' th' fleet.

ARIEL.   Safely in harbor
Is the King's ship; in the deep nook where once
Thou call'dst me up at midnight to fetch dew
From the still-vexed Bermoothes, there she's hid;
The mariners all under hatches stowed,   230
Who, with a charm joined to their suff'red labor,
I have left asleep; and for the rest o' th' fleet,
Which I dispersed, they all have met again,
And are upon the Mediterranean flote
Bound sadly home for Naples,
Supposing that they saw the King's ship wracked
And his great person perish.

PROSPERO.   Ariel, thy charge
Exactly is performed; but there's more work.
What is the time o' th' day?

---

212. *afire with me,* (refers either to the vessel or to Ferdinand, depending on the punctuation; F suggests the latter)
213. *up-staring,* standing on end
218. *sustaining,* buoying them up in the water
224. *this,* (illustrated by a gesture)
229. *still-vexed Bermoothes,* constantly agitated Bermudas
231. *suff'red,* undergone
234. *flote,* sea

ARIEL. Past the mid season.

PROSPERO. At least two glasses. The time 'twixt six and now   240
  Must by us both be spent most preciously.

ARIEL. Is there more toil? Since thou dost give me pains,
  Let me remember thee what thou hast promised,
  Which is not yet performed me.

PROSPERO. How now? moody?
  What is't thou canst demand?

ARIEL. My liberty.

PROSPERO. Before the time be out? No more!

ARIEL. I prithee,
  Remember I have done thee worthy service,
  Told thee no lies, made no mistakings, served
  Without or grudge or grumblings. Thou did promise
  To bate me a full year.

PROSPERO. Dost thou forget   250
  From what a torment I did free thee?

ARIEL. No.

PROSPERO. Thou dost; and think'st it much to tread the ooze
  Of the salt deep,
  To run upon the sharp wind of the North,
  To do me business in the veins o' th' earth
  When it is baked with frost.

ARIEL. I do not, sir.

PROSPERO. Thou liest, malignant thing! Hast thou forgot
  The foul witch Sycorax, who with age and envy
  Was grown into a hoop? Hast thou forgot her?

ARIEL. No, sir.

PROSPERO. Thou hast. Where was she born? Speak! Tell me!   260

ARIEL. Sir, in Argier.

PROSPERO. O, was she so? I must

---

239. *mid season,* noon
240. *glasses,* hours
243. *remember,* remind
246. *time,* period of service
248. *made,* (F reads 'made thee')
250. *bate me,* shorten my term of service
255. *veins,* streams
256. *baked,* hardened
258. *Sycorax,* (name not found elsewhere; usually connected with Greek *sys,* sow, and *korax,* which means both raven—cf. l. 322—and curved, hence perhaps 'hoop'); *envy,* malice
261. *Argier,* Algiers

Once in a month recount what thou hast been,
Which thou forget'st. This damned witch Sycorax,
For mischiefs manifold, and sorceries terrible
To enter human hearing, from Argier,
Thou know'st, was banished. For one thing she did
They would not take her life. Is not this true?

ARIEL. Ay, sir.

PROSPERO. This blue-eyed hag was hither brought with child
  And here was left by th' sailors. Thou, my slave,   270
  As thou report'st thyself, wast then her servant;
  And, for thou wast a spirit too delicate
  To act her earthy and abhorred commands,
  Refusing her grand hests, she did confine thee,
  By help of her more potent ministers,
  And in her most unmitigable rage,
  Into a cloven pine; within which rift
  Imprisoned thou didst painfully remain
  A dozen years; within which space she died
  And left thee there, where thou didst vent thy groans   280
  As fast as millwheels strike. Then was this island
  (Save for the son that she did litter here,
  A freckled whelp, hag-born) not honored with
  A human shape.

ARIEL.   Yes, Caliban her son.

PROSPERO. Dull thing, I say so: he, that Caliban
  Whom now I keep in service. Thou best know'st
  What torment I did find thee in: thy groans
  Did make wolves howl and penetrate the breasts
  Of ever-angry bears. It was a torment
  To lay upon the damned, which Sycorax   290
  Could not again undo. It was mine art,
  When I arrived and heard thee, that made gape
  The pine, and let thee out.

ARIEL.   I thank thee, master.

PROSPERO. If thou more murmur'st, I will rend an oak
  And peg thee in his knotty entrails till
  Thou hast howled away twelve winters.

---

266. *one thing she did,* (being pregnant, her sentence was commuted from death to exile)
274. *hests,* commands
281. *millwheels,* i.e., the clappers on the millwheels
295. *his,* its
296. *twelve,* (the same length of time that Ariel has been released)

ARIEL.   Pardon, master.
　　I will be correspondent to command
　　And do my spriting gently.
PROSPERO.   Do so; and after two days
　　I will discharge thee.
ARIEL.   That's my noble master!
　　What shall I do? Say what? What shall I do?   300
PROSPERO. Go make thyself like a nymph o' th' sea. Be subject
　　To no sight but thine and mine; invisible
　　To every eyeball else. Go take this shape
　　And hither come in't. Go! Hence with dilgence!   *Exit Ariel.*
　　Awake, dear heart, awake! Thou hast slept well.
　　Awake!
MIRANDA.   The strangeness of your story put
　　Heaviness in me.
PROSPERO.   Shake it off. Come on.
　　We'll visit Caliban, my slave, who never
　　Yields us kind answer.
MIRANDA.   'Tis a villain, sir,
　　I do not love to look on.
PROSPERO.   But as 'tis,   310
　　We cannot miss him: he does make our fire,
　　Fetch in our wood, and serves in offices
　　That profit us. What, ho! slave! Caliban!
　　Thou earth, thou! Speak!
CALIBAN. (*within*)   There's wood enough within.
PROSPERO. Come forth, I say! There's other business for thee.
　　Come, thou tortoise! When?

Enter ARIEL *like a water nymph.*

　　Fine apparition! My quaint Ariel,
　　Hark in thine ear.
ARIEL.   My lord, it shall be done.   *Exit.*
PROSPERO. Thou poisonous slave, got by the devil himself
　　Upon thy wicked dam, come forth!   320

---

297. *correspondent*, obedient
298. *spriting gently*, office as a spirit graciously
311. *miss*, do without
316. *When*, (expression of impatience)
317. *quaint*, ingenious

Enter CALIBAN.

CALIBAN. As wicked dew as e'er my mother brushed
  With raven's feather from unwholesome fen
  Drop on you both! A south-west blow on ye
  And blister you all o'er!
PROSPERO. For this, be sure, to-night thou shalt have cramps,
  Side-stitches that shall pen thy breath up; urchins
  Shall, for that vast of night that they may work,
  All exercise on thee; thou shalt be pinched
  As thick as honeycomb, each pinch more stinging
  Than bees that made 'em.
CALIBAN.   I must eat my dinner.   330
  This island's mine by Sycorax my mother,
  Which thou tak'st from me. When thou cam'st first,
  Thou strok'st me and made much of me; wouldst give me
  Water with berries in't; and teach me how
  To name the bigger light, and how the less,
  That burn by day and night; and then I loved thee
  And showed thee all the qualities o' th' isle,
  The fresh springs, brine-pits, barren place and fertile.
  Cursed be I that did so! All the charms
  Of Sycorax—toads, beetles, bats, light on you!   340
  For I am all the subjects that you have,
  Which first was mine own king; and here you sty me
  In this hard rock, whiles you do keep from me
  The rest o' th' island.
PROSPERO.   Thou most lying slave,
  Whom stripes may move, not kindness! I have used thee
  (Filth as thou art) with humane care, and lodged thee
  In mine own cell till thou didst seek to violate
  The honor of my child.
CALIBAN. O ho, O ho! Would't had been done!
  Thou didst prevent me; I had peopled else   350
  This isle with Calibans.
MIRANDA.   Abhorrèd slave,

---

326. *urchins,* hedgehogs (i.e., goblins in that shape)
327. *vast,* void; *that they may work,* (referring to the belief that malignant spirits had power only during darkness)
337. *qualities,* resources
345. *stripes,* lashes
351. *Miranda,* (so F; some editors have given the speech to Prospero)

Which any print of goodness wilt not take,
Being capable of all ill! I pitied thee,
Took pains to make thee speak, taught thee each hour
One thing or other: when thou didst not, savage,
Know thine own meaning, but wouldst gabble like
A thing most brutish, I endowed thy purposes
With words that made them known. But thy vile race,
Though thou didst learn, had that in't which good natures
Could not abide to be with; therefore wast thou   360
Deservedly confined into this rock, who hadst
Deserved more than a prison.
CALIBAN. You taught me language, and my profit on't
Is, I know how to curse. The red plague rid you
For learning me your language!
PROSPERO.   Hag-seed, hence!
Fetch us in fuel; and be quick, thou'rt best,
To answer other business. Shrug'st thou, malice?
If thou neglect'st or dost unwillingly
What I command, I'll rack thee with old cramps,
Fill all thy bones with aches, make thee roar   370
That beasts shall tremble at thy din.
CALIBAN.   No, pray thee.
(*Aside*) I must obey. His art is of such pow'r
It would control my dam's god, Setebos,
And make a vassal of him.
PROSPERO.   So, slave; hence!   *Exit Caliban.*

Enter FERDINAND; *and* ARIEL (*invisible*), *playing and singing.*

Ariel's song.

Come unto these yellow sands,
    And then take hands.
Curtsied when you have and kissed,
    The wild waves whist,

---

357. *purposes*, meanings
358. *race*, nature
359. *good natures*, natural virtues
364. *red plague*, bubonic plague; *rid*, destroy
366. *thou'rt best*, you'd be well advised
369. *old*, i.e., such as old people have
370. *aches*, (pronounced 'aitches')
378. *whist*, being hushed

Foot it featly here and there;
And, sweet sprites, the burden bear.   380
   Hark, hark!
     Burden, dispersedly. Bowgh, wawgh!
   The watchdogs bark.
     Burden, dispersedly. Bowgh, wawgh!
   Hark, hark! I hear
   The strain of strutting chanticleer
     Cry cock-a-diddle-dowe.

FERDINAND. Where should this music be? I' th' air or th' earth?
  It sounds no more; and sure it waits upon
  Some god o' th' island. Sitting on a bank,   390
  Weeping again the King my father's wrack,
  This music crept by me upon the waters,
  Allaying both their fury and my passion
  With its sweet air. Thence I have followed it,
  Or it hath drawn me rather; but 'tis gone.
  No, it begins again.

               Ariel's song.

Full fathom five thy father lies;
   Of his bones are coral made;
Those are pearls that were his eyes;
   Nothing of him that doth fade   400
But doth suffer a sea-change
Into something rich and strange.
Sea nymphs hourly ring his knell:
         Burden. Ding-dong.
Hark, now I hear them—Ding-dong bell.

FERDINAND. The ditty does remember my drowned father.
  This is no mortal business, nor no sound
  That the earth owes. I hear it now above me.
PROSPERO. The fringèd curtains of thine eye advance
  And say what thou seest yond.
MIRANDA.   What is't? a spirit?   410
  Lord, how it looks about! Believe me, sir,

---

379. *featly*, nimbly
380. *the burden bear*, (F has 'beare the burthen') ; *burden*, undersong, refrain
393. *passion*, lamentation
406. *remember*, allude to
408. *owes*, owns
409. *advance*, raise

It carries a brave form. But 'tis a spirit.

PROSPERO. No, wench: it eats, and sleeps, and hath such senses
As we have, such. This gallant which thou seest
Was in the wrack; and, but he's something stained
With grief (that's beauty's canker), thou mightst call him
A goodly person. He hath lost his fellows
And strays about to find 'em.

MIRANDA.   I might call him
A thing divine; for nothing natural
I ever saw so noble.

PROSPERO.   *(aside)* It goes on, I see,   420
As my soul prompts it. Spirit, fine spirit, I'll free thee
Within two days for this.

FERDINAND.   Most sure, the goddess
On whom these airs attend! Vouchsafe my prayer
May know if you remain upon this island,
And that you will some good instruction give
How I may bear me here. My prime request,
Which I do last pronounce, is (O you wonder!)
If you be maid or no?

MIRANDA.   No wonder, sir,
But certainly a maid.

FERDINAND.   My language? Heavens!
I am the best of them that speak this speech,   430
Were I but where 'tis spoken.

PROSPERO.   How? the best?
What wert thou if the King of Naples heard thee?

FERDINAND. A single thing, as I am now, that wonders
To hear thee speak of Naples. He does hear me;
And that he does I weep. Myself am Naples,
Who with mine eyes, never since at ebb, beheld
The King my father wracked.

MIRANDA.   Alack, for mercy!

FERDINAND. Yes, faith, and all his lords, the Duke of Milan
And his brave son being twain.

---

415. *stained,* disfigured
421. *prompts,* would like
422. *Most sure,* this is certainly
424. *remain,* dwell
426. *bear me,* conduct myself
433. *single,* (1) solitary (2) weak or helpless
435. *Naples,* King of Naples
439. *son,* (Antonio's son is not elsewhere mentioned)

PROSPERO.   (*aside*) The Duke of Milan   440
   And his more braver daughter could control thee,
   If now 'twere fit to do't. At the first sight
   They have changed eyes. Delicate Ariel,
   I'll set thee free for this.—A word, good sir.
   I fear you have done yourself some wrong. A word!
MIRANDA. Why speaks my father so ungently? This
   Is the third man that e'er I saw; the first
   That e'er I sighed for. Pity move my father
   To be inclined my way!
FERDINAND.   O, if a virgin,
   And your affection not gone forth, I'll make you
   The Queen of Naples.
PROSPERO.   Soft, sir! one word more.   450
   (*Aside*) They are both in either's pow'rs. But this swift business
   I must uneasy make, lest too light winning
   Make the prize light.—One word more! I charge thee
   That thou attend me. Thou dost here usurp
   The name thou ow'st not, and hast put thyself
   Upon this island as a spy, to win it
   From me, the lord on't.
FERDINAND.   No, as I am a man!
MIRANDA. There's nothing ill can dwell in such a temple.
   If the ill spirit have so fair a house,
   Good things will strive to dwell with't.
PROSPERO.   Follow me.—   460
   Speak not you for him; he's a traitor—Come!
   I'll manacle thy neck and feet together;
   Sea water shalt thou drink; thy food shall be
   The fresh-brook mussels, withered roots, and husks
   Wherein the acorn cradled. Follow!
FERDINAND.   No.
   I will resist such entertainment till
   Mine enemy has more power.
               He draws, and is charmed from moving.
MIRANDA.   O dear father,

---

440. *control*, refute
442. *changed eyes*, exchanged love looks
444. *done . . . wrong*, told a lie
455. *ow'st*, ownest
466. *entertainment*, treatment

Make not too rash a trial of him, for
He's gentle, and not fearful.
PROSPERO.   What, I say,
My foot my tutor?—Put thy sword up, traitor!   470
Who mak'st a show but dar'st not strike, thy conscience
Is so possessed with guilt. Come, from thy ward!
For I can here disarm thee with this stick
And make thy weapon drop.
MIRANDA.   Beseech you, father!
PROSPERO. Hence! Hang not on my garments.
MIRANDA.   Sir, have pity.
I'll be his surety.
PROSPERO.   Silence! One word more
Shall make me chide thee, if not hate thee. What,
An advocate for an impostor? Hush!
Thou think'st there is no more such shapes as he,
Having seen but him and Caliban. Foolish wench!   480
To th' most of men this is a Caliban,
And they to him are angels.
MIRANDA.   My affections
Are then most humble. I have no ambition
To see a goodlier man.
PROSPERO.   Come on, obey!
Thy nerves are in their infancy again
And have no vigor in them.
FERDINAND.   So they are.
My spirits, as in a dream, are all bound up.
My father's loss, the weakness which I feel,
The wrack of all my friends, nor this man's threats
To whom I am subdued, are but light to me,   490
Might I but through my prison once a day
Behold this maid. All corners else o' th' earth
Let liberty make use of. Space enough
Have I in such a prison.
PROSPERO.   (*aside*) It works. (*to Ferdinand*)

---

468. *trial,* judgment
469. *gentle,* noble; *fearful,* cowardly
470. *My . . . tutor,* i.e., instructed by my underling
472. *ward,* fighting posture
482. *affections,* inclinations
484. *obey,* follow
485. *nerves,* sinews, tendons

Come on.——
Thou hast done well, fine Ariel! (*to Ferdinand*) Follow me.
(*To Ariel*) Hark what thou else shalt do me.

MIRANDA.   Be of comfort.
My father's of a better nature, sir,
Than he appears by speech. This is unwonted
Which now came from him.

PROSPERO.   Thou shalt be as free
As mountain winds; but then exactly do   500
All points of my command.

ARIEL.   To th' syllable.

PROSPERO. Come, follow.——Speak not for him.   *Exeunt.*

ACT II

SCENE 1

Enter ALONSO, SEBASTIAN, ANTONIO, GONZALO, ADRIAN,
FRANCISCO, *and others.*

GONZALO. Beseech you, sir, be merry. You have cause
(So have we all) of joy; for our escape
Is much beyond our loss. Our hint of woe
Is common: every day some sailor's wife,
The master of some merchant, and the merchant,
Have just our theme of woe; but for the miracle,
I mean our preservation, few in millions
Can speak like us. Then wisely, good sir, weigh
Our sorrow with our comfort.

ALONSO.   Prithee peace.

SEBASTIAN. He receives comfort like cold porridge.   10

ANTONIO. The visitor will not give him o'er so.

SEBASTIAN. Look, he's winding up the watch of his wit; by and by it
    will strike.

---

500. *then,* till then
3. *hint,* occasion
5. *master of some merchant,* master of a merchant ship; *the merchant,* the owner of
the ship
10. *porridge,* (pun on 'peace' [pease])
11. *visitor,* spiritual adviser; *give him o'er,* let him alone

GONZALO. Sir—

SEBASTIAN. One. Tell.

GONZALO. When every grief is entertained, that's offered
  Comes to th' entertainer—

SEBASTIAN. A dollar.

GONZALO. Dolor comes to him, indeed. You have spoken truer than
  you purposed.   20

SEBASTIAN. You have taken it wiselier than I meant you should.

GONZALO. Therefore, my lord—

ANTONIO. Fie, what a spendthrift is he of his tongue!

ALONSO. I prithee spare.

GONZALO. Well, I have done. But yet—

SEBASTIAN. He will be talking.

ANTONIO. Which, of he or Adrian, for a good wager, first begins to
  crow?

SEBASTIAN. The old cock.

ANTONIO. The cock'rel.   30

SEBASTIAN. Done! The wager?

ANTONIO. A laughter.

SEBASTIAN. A match!

ADRIAN. Though this island seem to be desert—

ANTONIO. Ha, ha, ha!

SEBASTIAN. So, you're paid.

ADRIAN. Uninhabitable and almost inaccessible—

SEBASTIAN. Yet—

ADRIAN. Yet—

ANTONIO. He could not miss't.   40

ADRIAN. It must needs be of subtle, tender, and delicate temperance.

ANTONIO. Temperance was a delicate wench.

SEBASTIAN. Ay, and a subtle, as he most learnedly delivered.

ADRIAN. The air breathes upon us here most sweetly.

SEBASTIAN. As if it had lungs, and rotten ones.

ANTONIO. Or as 'twere perfumed by a fen.

---

15. *Tell*, count
16. *that's*, that which is
17. *entertainer*, (taken by Sebastian to mean 'innkeeper')
19. *Dolor*, grief (with pun on 'dollar,' a continental coin)
23. *spendthrift*, (Antonio labors the pun)
29. *old cock*, i.e., Gonzalo
30. *cock'rel*, i.e., Adrian
32. *laughter*, the winner laughs
35–36. (speakers reversed in F)
41. *temperance*, climate
42. *Temperance*, (a girl's name)

GONZALO. Here is everything advantageous to life.

ANTONIO. True; save means to live.

SEBASTIAN. Of that there's none, or little.

GONZALO. How lush and lusty the grass looks! how green!   50

ANTONIO. The ground indeed is tawny.

SEBASTIAN. With an eye of green in't.

ANTONIO. He misses not much.

SEBASTIAN. No; he doth but mistake the truth totally.

GONZALO. But the rarity of it is—which is indeed almost beyond credit—

SEBASTIAN. As many vouched rarities are.

GONZALO. That our garments, being, as they were, drenched in the sea, hold, notwithstanding, their freshness and gloss, being rather new-dyed than stained with salt water.   60

ANTONIO. If but one of his pockets could speak, would it not say he lies?

SEBASTIAN. Ay, or very falsely pocket up his report.

GONZALO. Methinks our garments are now as fresh as when we put them on first in Afric, at the marriage of the King's fair daughter Claribel to the King of Tunis.

SEBASTIAN. 'Twas a sweet marriage, and we prosper well in our return.

ADRIAN. Tunis was never graced before with such a paragon to their queen.   70

GONZALO. Not since widow Dido's time.

ANTONIO. Widow? A pox o' that! How came that 'widow' in? Widow Dido!

SEBASTIAN. What if he had said 'widower Aeneas' too? Good Lord, how you take it!

ADRIAN. 'Widow Dido,' said you? You make me study of that. She was of Carthage, not of Tunis.

GONZALO. This Tunis, sir, was Carthage.

ADRIAN. Carthage?

GONZALO. I assure you, Carthage.   80

ANTONIO. His word is more than the miraculous harp.

---

52. *eye*, spot (or perhaps Gonzalo's eye)

57. *vouched rarities*, wonders guaranteed to be true

69. *to*, for

71. *widow Dido*, (Dido was the widow of Sychaeus; Aeneas was a widower, having lost his wife in the fall of Troy. The reasons for Antonio's amusement, if that is what it is, have not been explained.)

81. *miraculous harp*, (of Amphion, which raised the walls of Thebes; Tunis and Carthage were near each other, but not the same city)

SEBASTIAN. He hath raised the wall and houses too.

ANTONIO. What impossible matter will he make easy next?

SEBASTIAN. I think he will carry this island home in his pocket and
give it his son for an apple.

ANTONIO. And, sowing the kernels of it in the sea, bring forth more
islands.

GONZALO. Ay!

ANTONIO. Why, in good time.

GONZALO. Sir, we were talking that our garments seem now as fresh   90
as when we were at Tunis at the marriage of your daughter, who
is now Queen.

ANTONIO. And the rarest that e'er came there.

SEBASTIAN. Bate, I beseech you, widow Dido.

ANTONIO. O, widow Dido? Ay, widow Dido!

GONZALO. Is not, sir, my doublet as fresh as the first day I wore it?
I mean, in a sort.

ANTONIO. That 'sort' was well fished for.

GONZALO. When I wore it at your daughter's marriage.

ALONSO. You cram these words into mine ears against   100
The stomach of my sense. Would I had never
Married my daughter there! for, coming thence,
My son is lost; and, in my rate, she too,
Who is so far from Italy removed
I ne'er again shall see her. O thou mine heir
Of Naples and of Milan, what strange fish
Hath made his meal on thee?

FRANCISCO.   Sir, he may live.
I saw him beat the surges under him
And ride upon their backs. He trod the water,
Whose enmity he flung aside, and breasted   110
The surge most swol'n that met him. His bold head
'Bove the contentious waves he kept, and oared
Himself with his good arms in lusty stroke
To th' shore that o'er his wave-worn basis bowed,
As stooping to relieve him. I not doubt
He came alive to land.

---

88. *Ay*, (F reads 'I'; this and Antonio's rejoinder have not been satisfactorily
explained)

94. *Bate*, except

97. *in a sort*, i.e., comparatively

101. *stomach . . . sense*, i.e., inclination of my mind

103. *rate*, opinion

114. *his*, its; *basis*, i.e., the sand

ALONSO. No, no, he's gone.

SEBASTIAN. Sir, you may thank yourself for this great loss,
  That would not bless our Europe with your daughter,
  But rather loose her to an African,
  Where she, at least, is banished from your eye   120
  Who hath cause to wet the grief on't.

ALONSO. Prithee peace.

SEBASTIAN. You were kneeled to and importuned otherwise
  By all of us; and the fair soul herself
  Weighed, between loathness and obedience, at
  Which end o' th' beam should bow. We have lost your son,
  I fear, for ever. Milan and Naples have
  Moe widows in them of this business' making
  Than we bring men to comfort them:
  The fault's your own.

ALONSO. So is the dear'st o' th' loss.

GONZALO. My Lord Sebastian,   130
  The truth you speak doth lack some gentleness,
  And time to speak it in. You rub the sore
  When you should bring the plaster.

SEBASTIAN. Very well.

ANTONIO. And most chirurgeonly.

GONZALO. It is foul weather in us all, good sir,
  When you are cloudy.

SEBASTIAN. Foul weather?

ANTONIO. Very foul.

GONZALO. Had I plantation of this isle, my lord—

ANTONIO. He'd sow't with nettle seed.

SEBASTIAN. Or docks, or mallows.

GONZALO. And were the king on't, what would I do?

SEBASTIAN. Scape being drunk for want of wine.   140

GONZALO. I' th' commonwealth I would by contraries
  Execute all things; for no kind of traffic
  Would I admit; no name of magistrate;

123–25. *the fair . . . bow,* (the sense is that Claribel hated the marriage, and only obedience to her father turned the scale)
  127. *Moe,* more
  129. *dear'st,* heaviest
  134. *chirurgeonly,* like a surgeon
  137. *plantation,* colonization (taken by Antonio in its other sense)
  141. *by contraries,* in contrast to usual customs
  142. *traffic,* trade

Letters should not be known; riches, poverty,
And use of service, none; contract, succession,
Bourn, bound of land, tilth, vineyard, none;
No use of metal, corn, or wine, or oil;
No occupation; all men idle, all;
And women too, but innocent and pure;
No sovereignty.

SEBASTIAN.   Yet he would be king on't.   150

ANTONIO. The latter end of his commonwealth forgets the beginning.

GONZALO. All things in common nature should produce
Without sweat or endeavor. Treason, felony,
Sword, pike, knife, gun, or need of any engine
Would I not have; but nature should bring forth,
Of it own kind, all foison, all abundance,
To feed my innocent people.

SEBASTIAN. No marrying 'mong his subjects?

ANTONIO. None, man, all idle—whores and knaves.

GONZALO. I would with such perfection govern, sir,   160
T' excel the golden age.

SEBASTIAN.   Save his Majesty!

ANTONIO. Long live Gonzalo!

GONZALO.   And—do you mark me, sir?

ALONSO. Prithee no more. Thou dost talk nothing to me.

GONZALO. I do well believe your Highness; and did it to minister occasion to these gentlemen, who are of such sensible and nimble lungs that they always use to laugh at nothing.

ANTONIO. 'Twas you we laughed at.

GONZALO. Who in this kind of merry fooling am nothing to you: so you may continue, and laugh at nothing still.

ANTONIO. What a blow was there given!   170

SEBASTIAN. An it had not fall'n flatlong.

GONZALO. You are gentlemen of brave mettle; you would lift the moon out of her sphere if she would continue in it five weeks without changing.

---

145. *use of service*, having a servant class; *succession*, inheritance
146. *Bourn*, limits of private property
154. *engine*, weapon
156. *it*, its; *foison*, abundance
164–65. *minister occasion*, afford opportunity
165. *sensible*, sensitive
171. *An*, if; *flatlong*, struck with the flat of a sword

Enter ARIEL, (*invisible,*) *playing solemn music.*

SEBASTIAN. We would so, and then go a-batfowling.

ANTONIO. Nay, good my lord, be not angry.

GONZALO. No, I warrant you: I will not adventure my discretion so
weakly. Will you laugh me asleep, for I am very heavy?

ANTONIO. Go sleep, and hear us.

        (*All sleep except Alonso, Sebastian, and Antonio.*)

ALONSO. What, all so soon asleep? I wish mine eyes   180
Would, with themselves, shut up my thoughts. I find
They are inclined to do so.

SEBASTIAN.   Please you, sir,
Do not omit the heavy offer of it.
It seldom visits sorrow; when it doth,
It is a comforter.

ANTONIO.   We two, my lord,
Will guard your person while you take your rest,
And watch your safety.

ALONSO.   Thank you. Wondrous heavy.

        (*Alonso sleeps. Exit Ariel.*)

SEBASTIAN. What a strange drowsiness possesses them!

ANTONIO. It is the quality o' th' climate.

SEBASTIAN.   Why
Doth it not then our eyelids sink? I find not   190
Myself disposed to sleep.

ANTONIO.   Nor I: my spirits are nimble.
They fell together all, as by consent.
They dropped as by a thunder-stroke. What might,
Worthy Sebastian—O, what might?—No more!
And yet methinks I see it in thy face,
What thou shouldst be. Th' occasion speaks thee, and
My strong imagination sees a crown
Dropping upon thy head.

SEBASTIAN.   What? Art thou waking?

ANTONIO. Do you not hear me speak?

SEBASTIAN.   I do; and surely

---

175. *a-batfowling,* hunting birds with sticks ('bats') at night (using the moon for a
lantern)

177. *adventure,* risk (Gonzalo is saying, very politely, that their wit is too feeble for
him to take offense at it)

183. *omit,* neglect; *heavy offer,* the opportunity its heaviness affords

196. *speaks,* speaks to, summons

It is a sleepy language, and thou speak'st   200
Out of thy sleep. What is it thou didst say?
This is a strange repose, to be asleep
With eyes wide open; standing, speaking, moving,
And yet so fast asleep.
ANTONIO.   Noble Sebastian,
Thou let'st thy fortune sleep—die, rather; wink'st
Whiles thou art waking.
SEBASTIAN.   Thou dost snore distinctly;
There's meaning in thy snores.
ANTONIO. I am more serious than my custom. You
Must be so too, if heed me; which to do
Trebles thee o'er.
SEBASTIAN.   Well, I am standing water.   210
ANTONIO. I'll teach you how to flow.
SEBASTIAN.   Do so. To ebb
Hereditary sloth instructs me.
ANTONIO.   O,
If you but knew how you the purpose cherish
Whiles thus you mock it! how, in stripping it,
You more invest it! Ebbing men indeed
(Most often) do so near the bottom run
By their own fear or sloth.
SEBASTIAN.   Prithee say on.
The setting of thine eye and cheek proclaim
A matter from thee; and a birth, indeed,
Which throes thee much to yield.
ANTONIO.   Thus, sir: 220
Although this lord of weak remembrance, this
Who shall be of as little memory
When he is earthed, hath here almost persuaded
(For he's a spirit of persuasion, only
Professes to persuade) the King his son's alive,

---

205. *wink'st,* dost sleep
210. *Trebles thee o'er,* increases thy status threefold; *standing water,* at slack tide
212. *Hereditary sloth,* natural laziness
213. *cherish,* enrich
215. *invest,* clothe
220. *throes thee much,* costs thee much pain, like a birth
221. *remembrance,* memory
222. *of . . . memory,* as little remembered
223. *earthed,* buried
225. *Professes,* has the function

'Tis as impossible that he's undrowned
As he that sleeps here swims.

SEBASTIAN.   I have no hope
That he's undrowned.

ANTONIO.   O, out of that no hope
What great hope have you! No hope that way is
Another way so high a hope that even   230
Ambition cannot pierce a wink beyond,
But doubt discovery there. Will you grant with me
That Ferdinand is drowned?

SEBASTIAN.   He's gone.

ANTONIO.   Then tell me,
Who's the next heir of Naples?

SEBASTIAN.   Claribel.

ANTONIO. She that is Queen of Tunis; she that dwells
Ten leagues beyond man's life; she that from Naples
Can have no note, unless the sun were post—
The man i' th' moon's too slow—till new-born chins
Be rough and razorable; she that from whom
We all were sea-swallowed, though some cast again,   240
And, by that destiny, to perform an act
Whereof what's past is prologue, what to come,
In yours and my discharge.

SEBASTIAN.   What stuff is this? How say you?
'Tis true my brother's daughter's Queen of Tunis;
So is she heir of Naples; 'twixt which regions
There is some space.

ANTONIO.   A space whose ev'ry cubit
Seems to cry out 'How shall that Claribel
Measure us back to Naples? Keep in Tunis,
And let Sebastian wake!' Say this were death
That now hath seized them, why, they were no worse   250
Than now they are. There be that can rule Naples
As well as he that sleeps; lords that can prate
As amply and unnecessarily

---

231. *wink*, glimpse
232. *doubt discovery there*, is uncertain of seeing accurately
236. *Ten . . . life*, i.e., thirty miles from nowhere
237. *note*, communication; *post*, messenger
240. *cast*, thrown up (with a suggestion of its theatrical meaning which introduces the next metaphor)
243. *discharge*, business
248. *us*, i.e., the cubits

As this Gonzalo; I myself could make
A chough of as deep chat. O, that you bore
The mind that I do! What a sleep were this
For your advancement! Do you understand me?
SEBASTIAN. Methinks I do.
ANTONIO.   And how does your content
Tender your own good fortune?
SEBASTIAN.   I remember
You did supplant your brother Prospero.
ANTONIO.   True.   260
And look how well my garments sit upon me,
Much feater than before. My brother's servants
Were then my fellows; now they are my men.
SEBASTIAN. But, for your conscience—
ANTONIO. Ay, sir, where lies that? If 'twere a kibe,
'Twould put me to my slipper; but I feel not
This deity in my bosom. Twenty consciences
That stand 'twixt me and Milan, candied be they
And melt, ere they molest! Here lies your brother,
No better than the earth he lies upon   270
If he were that which now he's like—that's dead;
Whom I with this obedient steel (three inches of it)
Can lay to bed for ever; whiles you, doing thus,
To the perpetual wink for aye might put
This ancient morsel, this Sir Prudence, who
Should not upbraid our course. For all the rest,
They'll take suggestion as a cat laps milk;
They'll tell the clock to any business that
We say befits the hour.
SEBASTIAN.   Thy case, dear friend,
Shall be my precedent. As thou got'st Milan,   280
I'll come by Naples. Draw thy sword. One stroke
Shall free thee from the tribute which thou payest,
And the King shall love thee.

---

255. *chough*, jackdaw (a bird sometimes taught to speak)
258–59. *content Tender*, inclination estimate
262. *feater*, more suitable
263. *fellows*, equals; *men*, servants
265. *kibe*, chilblain
266. *put me to*, make me wear
268. *candied*, frozen
274. *wink*, sleep
278. *tell the clock*, answer appropriately

ANTONIO.   Draw together;
  And when I rear my hand, do you the like,
  To fall it on Gonzalo.   (*They draw.*)
SEBASTIAN.   O, but one word!

Enter ARIEL, (*invisible,*) *with music and song.*

ARIEL. My master through his art foresees the danger
  That you, his friend, are in, and sends me forth
  (For else his project dies) to keep them living.
                            Sings in Gonzalo's ear.
              While you here do snoring lie,
              Open-eyed conspiracy   290
                His time doth take.
              If of life you keep a care,
              Shake off slumber and beware.
                Awake, awake!
ANTONIO. Then let us both be sudden.
GONZALO. (*wakes*)   Now good angels
  Preserve the King!
ALONSO. Why, how now?—Ho, awake!—Why are you drawn?
  Wherefore this ghastly looking?
GONZALO.   What's the matter?
SEBASTIAN. Whiles we stood here securing your repose,
  Even now, we heard a hollow burst of bellowing   300
  Like bulls, or rather lions. Did't not wake you?
  It struck mine ear most terribly.
ALONSO.   I heard nothing.
ANTONIO. O, 'twas a din to fright a monster's ear,
  To make an earthquake! Sure it was the roar
  Of a whole herd of lions.
ALONSO.   Heard you this, Gonzalo?
GONZALO. Upon mine honor, sir, I heard a humming,
  And that a strange one too, which did awake me.
  I shaked you, sir, and cried. As mine eyes opened,
  I saw their weapons drawn. There was a noise,
  That's verily. 'Tis best we stand upon our guard,   310
  Or that we quit this place. Let's draw our weapons.
ALONSO. Lead off this ground, and let's make further search
  For my poor son.

---

285. *fall it*, let it fall
299. *securing*, keeping watch over

GONZALO.   Heavens keep him from these beasts!
  For he is sure i' th' island.
ALONSO.   Lead away.
ARIEL. Prospero my lord shall know what I have done.
  So, King, go safely on to seek thy son.   *Exeunt.*

SCENE 2

Enter CALIBAN *with a burden of wood. A noise of thunder heard.*

CALIBAN. All the infections that the sun sucks up
  From bogs, fens, flats, on Prosper fall, and make him
  By inchmeal a disease! His spirits hear me,
  And yet I needs must curse. But they'll nor pinch,
  Fright me with urchin-shows, pitch me i' th' mire,
  Nor lead me, like a firebrand, in the dark
  Out of my way, unless he bid 'em; but
  For every trifle are they set upon me;
  Sometime like apes that mow and chatter at me,
  And after bite me; then like hedgehogs which   10
  Lie tumbling in my barefoot way and mount
  Their pricks at my footfall; sometime am I
  All wound with adders, who with cloven tongues
  Do hiss me into madness.

Enter TRINCULO

                      Lo, now, lo!
  Here comes a spirit of his, and to torment me.
  For bringing wood in slowly. I'll fall flat.
  Perchance he will not mind me.   (*Lies down.*)
TRINCULO. Here's neither bush nor shrub to bear off any weather at
  all, and another storm brewing: I hear it sing i' th' wind. Yond
  same black cloud, yond huge one, looks like a foul bombard that   20
  would shed his liquor. If it should thunder as it did before, I

---

  3. *By inchmeal*, inch by inch
  4. *nor*, neither
  5. *urchin-shows*, apparitions in the form of hedgehogs
  6. *like a firebrand*, in the form of a will-o'-the-wisp
  9. *mow*, make faces
  18. *bear off*, ward off
  20. *bombard*, leather bottle
  21. *his*, its

know not where to hide my head. Yond same cloud cannot choose but fall by pailfuls. What have we here? a man or a fish? dead or alive? A fish: he smells like a fish; a very ancient and fishlike smell; a kind of not of the newest poor-John. A strange fish! Were I in England now, as once I was, and had but this fish painted, not a holiday fool there but would give a piece of silver. There would this monster make a man: any strange beast there makes a man. When they will not give a doit to relieve a lame beggar, they will lay out ten to see a dead Indian. Legged like   30 a man! and his fins like arms! Warm, o' my troth! I do now let loose my opinion, hold it no longer: this is no fish, but an islander, that hath lately suffered by a thunderbolt. (*Thunder.*) Alas, the storm is come again! My best way is to creep under his gaberdine: there is no other shelter hereabout. Misery acquaints a man with strange bedfellows. I will here shroud till the dregs of the storm be past.   (*Creeps under Caliban's garment.*)

Enter STEPHANO, *singing; (a bottle in his hand)*.

STEPHANO.   I shall no more to sea, to sea;
                        Here shall I die ashore.
This is a very scurvy tune to sing at a man's funeral. Well, here's   40
my comfort.   *Drinks.*
        The master, the swabber, the boatswain, and I,
            The gunner, and his mate,
    Loved Mall, Meg, and Marian, and Margery,
        But none of us cared for Kate.
        For she had a tongue with a tang,
        Would cry to a sailor 'Go hang!'
    She loved not the savor of tar nor of pitch;
    Yet a tailor might scratch her wher'er she did itch.
        Then to sea, boys, and let her go hang!   50
This is a scurvy tune too; but here's my comfort.   *Drinks.*
CALIBAN. Do not torment me! O!
STEPHANO. What's the matter? Have we devils here? Do you put tricks upon 's with savages and men of Inde, ha? I have not scaped drowning to be afeard now of your four legs; for it hath been

25. *poor-John*, dried hake
27. *painted*, i.e., on a signboard outside a booth at a fair
28. *make a man*, (also with sense of 'make a man's fortune')
29. *doit*, small coin
34–35. *gaberdine*, cloak

said, 'As proper a man as ever went on four legs cannot make him give ground'; and it shall be said so again, while Stephano breathes at nostrils.

CALIBAN. The spirit torments me. O!

STEPHANO. This is some monster of the isle, with four legs, who hath got, as I take it, an ague. Where the devil should he learn our language? I will give him some relief, if it be but for that. If I can recover him, and keep him tame, and get to Naples with him, he's a present for any emperor that ever trod on neat's leather.   60

CALIBAN. Do not torment me, prithee; I'll bring my wood home faster.

STEPHANO. He's in his fit now and does not talk after the wisest. He shall taste of my bottle: if he have never drunk wine afore, it will go near to remove his fit. If I can recover him and keep him tame, I will not take too much for him; he shall pay for him that hath him, and that soundly.   70

CALIBAN. Thou dost me yet but little hurt.

Thou wilt anon; I know it by thy trembling.

Now Prosper works upon thee.

STEPHANO. Come on your ways: open your mouth: here is that which will give language to you, cat. Open your mouth. This will shake your shaking, I can tell you, and that soundly. (*Gives Caliban drink.*) You cannot tell who's your friend. Open your chaps again.   80

TRINCULO. I should know that voice. It should be—but he is drowned; and these are devils. O, defend me!

STEPHANO. Four legs and two voices—a most delicate monster! His forward voice now is to speak well of his friend; his backward voice is to utter foul speeches and to detract. If all the wine in my bottle will recover him, I will help his ague. Come! (*Gives drink.*) Amen! I will pour some in thy other mouth.

TRINCULO. Stephano!

STEPHANO. Doth thy other mouth call me? Mercy, mercy! This is a devil, and no monster. I will leave him; I have no long spoon.   90

TRINCULO. Stephano! If thou beest Stephano, touch me and speak to

---

64–65. *neat's leather,* cowhide

71. *not take too much,* i.e., take all I can get

74. *anon,* soon

77. *cat,* (alluding to the proverb 'Liquor will make a cat talk')

79. *chaps,* jaws

90. *spoon,* (alluding to the proverb 'He who sups with the devil must have a long spoon')

me; for I am Trinculo—be not afeard—thy good friend Trinculo.

STEPHANO. If thou beest Trinculo, come forth. I'll pull thee by the lesser legs. If any be Trinculo's legs, these are they. (*Draws him out from under Caliban's garment.*) Thou art very Trinculo indeed: how cam'st thou to be the siege of this mooncalf? Can he vent Trinculos?

TRINCULO. I took him to be killed with a thunder-stroke. But art thou not drowned, Stephano? I hope now thou art not drowned. Is the storm overblown? I hid me under the dead mooncalf's 100 gaberdine for fear of the storm. And art thou living, Stephano? O Stephano, two Neapolitans scaped!

STEPHANO. Prithee do not turn me about: my stomach is not constant.

CALIBAN. (*aside*) These be fine things, an if they be not sprites.
That's a brave god and bears celestial liquor.
I will kneel to him.

STEPHANO. How didst thou scape? How cam'st thou hither? Swear by this bottle how thou cam'st hither. I escaped upon a butt of sack which the sailors heaved o'erboard, by this bottle, which I made of the bark of a tree with mine own hands since I was cast 110 ashore.

CALIBAN. I'll swear upon that bottle to be thy true subject, for the liquor is not earthly.

STEPHANO. Here! Swear then how thou escapedst.

TRINCULO. Swum ashore, man, like a duck. I can swim like a duck, I'll be sworn.

STEPHANO. Here, kiss the book. (*Gives him drink.*) Though thou canst swim like a duck, thou art made like a goose.

TRINCULO. O Stephano, hast any more of this?

STEPHANO. The whole butt, man: my cellar is in a rock by th' sea- 120 side, where my wine is hid. How now, mooncalf? How does thine ague?

CALIBAN. Hast thou not dropped from heaven?

STEPHANO. Out o' th' moon, I do assure thee. I was the Man i' th' Moon when time was.

CALIBAN. I have seen thee in her, and I do adore thee.
My mistress showed me thee, and thy dog, and thy bush.

STEPHANO. Come, swear to that; kiss the book. I will furnish it

---

96. *siege*, excrement; *mooncalf*, monstrosity
104. *an if*, if
117. *book*, i.e., bottle
118. *like a goose*, i.e., with a long neck
125. *when time was*, once upon a time

anon with new contents. Swear. (*Caliban drinks.*)

TRINCULO. By this good light, this is a very shallow monster! I 130
afeard of him? A very weak monster! The Man i' th' Moon? A
most poor credulous monster!—Well drawn, monster, in good
sooth!

CALIBAN. I'll show thee every fertile inch o' th' island;
And I will kiss thy foot. I prithee be my god.

TRINCULO. By this light, a most perfidious and drunken monster!
When God's asleep, he'll rob his bottle.

CALIBAN. I'll kiss thy foot. I'll swear myself thy subject.

STEPHANO. Come on then. Down, and swear!

TRINCULO. I shall laugh myself to death at this puppy-headed mon- 140
ster. A most scurvy monster! I could find in my heart to beat
him—

STEPHANO. Come, kiss.

TRINCULO. But that the poor monster's in drink. An abominable
monster!

CALIBAN. I'll show thee the best springs; I'll pluck thee berries.
I'll fish for thee, and get thee wood enough.
A plague upon the tyrant that I serve!
I'll bear him no more sticks, but follow thee,
Thou wondrous man. 150

TRINCULO. A most ridiculous monster, to make a wonder of a poor
drunkard!

CALIBAN. I prithee let me bring thee where crabs grow;
And I with my long nails will dig thee pignuts,
Show thee a jay's nest, and instruct thee how
To snare the nimble marmoset; I'll bring thee
To clust'ring filberts, and sometimes I'll get thee
Young scamels from the rock. Wilt thou go with me?

STEPHANO. I prithee, now, lead the way without any more talking.
Trinculo, the King and all our company else being drowned, we 160
will inherit thee. Here, bear my bottle. Fellow Trinculo, we'll
fill him by and by again. *Caliban sings drunkenly.*

CALIBAN. Farewell, master; farewell, farewell!

TRINCULO. A howling monster! a drunken monster!

CALIBAN. No more dams I'll make for fish,

---

153. *crabs,* crabapples
154. *pignuts,* peanuts
158. *scamels,* (unexplained, but clearly either a shellfish or a rock-nesting bird;
perhaps a misprint for 'seamels,' seamews)
161. *inherit,* take possession
162. *by and by,* soon

Nor fetch in firing
At requiring,
Nor scrape trenchering, nor wash dish.
'Ban, 'Ban, Ca—Caliban
Has a new master; get a new man.   170
Freedom, high-day! high-day, freedom; freedom, high-day, free-
dom!

STEPHANO. O brave monster! lead the way.   *Exeunt.*

ACT III

SCENE 1

Enter FERDINAND, *bearing a log.*

FERDINAND. There be some sports are painful, and their labor
Delight in them sets off; some kinds of baseness
Are nobly undergone, and most poor matters
Point to rich ends. This my mean task
Would be as heavy to me as odious, but
The mistress which I serve quickens what's dead
And makes my labors pleasures. O, she is
Ten times more gentle than her father's crabbèd;
And he's composed of harshness! I must remove
Some thousands of these logs and pile them up,   10
Upon a sore injunction. My sweet mistress
Weeps when she sees me work, and says such baseness
Had never like executor. I forget;
But these sweet thoughts do even refresh my labors
Most busy least, when I do it.

Enter MIRANDA; *and* PROSPERO (*behind, unseen*).

MIRANDA.   Alas, now pray you

---

168. *trenchering*, trenchers, wooden plates
1. *painful*, strenuous
2. *sets off*, makes greater by contrast
3. *matters*, affairs
6. *quickens*, brings to life
11. *sore injunction*, grievous command
15. *least*, i.e., least conscious of being busy (F reads 'lest')

Work not so hard! I would the lightning had
Burnt up those logs that you are enjoined to pile!
Pray set it down and rest you. When this burns,
'Twill weep for having wearied you. My father
Is hard at study: pray now rest yourself. 20
He's safe for these three hours.
FERDINAND.   O most dear mistress,
    The sun will set before I shall discharge
    What I must strive to do.
MIRANDA.   If you'll sit down,
    I'll bear your logs the while. Pray give me that:
    I'll carry it to the pile.
FERDINAND.   No, precious creature:
    I had rather crack my sinews, break my back,
    Than you should such dishonor undergo
    While I sit lazy by.
MIRANDA.   It would become me
    As well as it does you; and I should do it
    With much more ease; for my good will is to it, 30
    And yours it is against.
PROSPERO.   (*aside*) Poor worm, thou art infected!
    This visitation shows it.
MIRANDA.   You look wearily.
FERDINAND. No, noble mistress; 'tis fresh morning with me
    When you are by at night. I do beseech you,
    Chiefly that I might set it in my prayers,
    What is your name?
MIRANDA.   Miranda. O my father,
    I have broke your hest to say so!
FERDINAND.   Admired Miranda!
    Indeed the top of admiration, worth
    What's dearest to the world! Full many a lady
    I have eyed with best regard, and many a time 40
    Th' harmony of their tongues hath into bondage
    Brought my too diligent ear; for several virtues
    Have I liked several women; never any

---

19. *weep,* i.e., exude resin
32. *visitation,* (1) visit (2) attack of plague (in the metaphor of 'infected')
37. *hest,* command
38. *admiration,* wonder, astonishment (the name Miranda means wonderful woman; cf. I, ii, 427)
40. *best regard,* highest approval
42. *several,* different

With so full soul but some defect in her
Did quarrel with the noblest grace she owed,
And put it to the foil. But you, O you,
So perfect and so peerless, are created
Of every creature's best.
MIRANDA.   I do not know
One of my sex; no woman's face remember,
Save, from my glass, mine own; nor have I seen   50
More than I may call men than you, good friend,
And my dear father. How features are abroad
I am skilless of; but, by my modesty
(The jewel in my dower), I would not wish
Any companion in the world but you;
Nor can imagination form a shape,
Besides yourself, to like of. But I prattle
Something too wildly, and my father's precepts
I therein do forget.
FERDINAND.   I am, in my condition,
A prince, Miranda; I do think, a king   60
(I would not so), and would no more endure
This wooden slavery than to suffer
The fleshfly blow my mouth. Hear my soul speak!
The very instant that I saw you, did
My heart fly to your service; there resides,
To make me slave to it; and for your sake
Am I this patient log-man.
MIRANDA.   Do you love me?
FERDINAND. O heaven, O earth, bear witness to this sound,
And crown what I profess with kind event
If I speak true! if hollowly, invert   70
What best is boded me to mischief! I,
Beyond all limit of what else i' th' world,
Do love, prize, honor you.
MIRANDA.   I am a fool
To weep at what I am glad of.

---

44. *with . . . soul*, i.e., so wholeheartedly
45. *owed*, owned
46. *foil*, (1) overthrow (2) contrast
52. *abroad*, elsewhere
53. *skilless*, ignorant
57. *like of*, compare to
59. *condition*, situation in the world
69. *kind event*, favorable outcome

PROSPERO.   (*aside*) Fair encounter
  Of two most rare affections! Heavens rain grace
  On that which breeds between 'em!
FERDINAND.   Wherefore weep you?
MIRANDA. At mine unworthiness, that dare not offer
  What I desire to give, and much less take
  What I shall die to want. But this is trifling;
  And all the more it seeks to hide itself,   80
  The bigger bulk it shows. Hence, bashful cunning,
  And prompt me, plain and holy innocence!
  I am your wife, if you will marry me;
  If not, I'll die your maid. To be your fellow
  You may deny me; but I'll be your servant,
  Whether you will or no.
FERDINAND.   My mistress, dearest,
  And I thus humble ever.
MIRANDA.   My husband then?
FERDINAND. Ay, with a heart as willing
  As bondage e'er of freedom. Here's my hand.
MIRANDA. And mine, with my heart in't; and now farewell   90
  Till half an hour hence.
FERDINAND.   A thousand thousand!
                    Exeunt (Ferdinand and Miranda severally).
PROSPERO. So glad of this as they I cannot be,
  Who are surprised withal; but my rejoicing
  At nothing can be more. I'll to my book;
  For yet ere supper time must I perform
  Much business appertaining.   *Exit.*

SCENE 2

Enter CALIBAN, STEPHANO, *and* TRINCULO.

STEPHANO. Tell not me! When the butt is out, we will drink water;
  not a drop before. Therefore bear up and board 'em! Servant
  monster, drink to me.

---

79. *want,* lack
81. *bashful cunning,* i.e., coyness
84. *fellow,* equal
89. *of freedom,* i.e., to win freedom
93. *surprised withal,* taken unaware by it
96. *appertaining,* relevant
2. *bear . . . 'em,* i.e., drink up (Caliban has almost 'passed out')

TRINCULO. Servant monster? The folly of this island! They say there's
but five upon this isle: we are three of them. If th' other two be
brained like us, the state totters.

STEPHANO. Drink, servant monster, when I bid thee: thy eyes are almost set in thy head.

TRINCULO. Where should they be set else? He were a brave monster
indeed if they were set in his tail.   10

STEPHANO. My man-monster hath drowned his tongue in sack. For
my part, the sea cannot drown me. I swam, ere I could recover the
shore, five-and-thirty leagues off and on, by this light. Thou shalt
be my lieutenant, monster, or my standard.

TRINCULO. Your lieutenant, if you list; he's no standard.

STEPHANO. We'll not run, Monsieur Monster.

TRINCULO. Nor go neither; but you'll lie like dogs, and yet say nothing neither.

STEPHANO. Mooncalf, speak once in thy life, if thou beest a good
mooncalf.   20

CALIBAN. How does thy honor? Let me lick thy shoe.
I'll not serve him; he is not valiant.

TRINCULO. Thou liest, most ignorant monster: I am in case to justle
a constable. Why, thou deboshed fish thou, was there ever man a
coward that hath drunk so much sack as I to-day? Wilt thou tell a
monstrous lie, being but half a fish and half a monster?

CALIBAN. Lo, how he mocks me! Wilt thou let him, my lord?

TRINCULO. 'Lord' quoth he? That a monster should be such a natural!

CALIBAN. Lo, lo, again! Bite him to death, I prithee.

STEPHANO. Trinculo, keep a good tongue in your head. If you prove   30
a mutineer—the next tree! The poor monster's my subject, and he
shall not suffer indignity.

CALIBAN. I thank my noble lord. Wilt thou be pleased
To hearken once again to the suit I made to thee?

STEPHANO. Marry, will I. Kneel and repeat it; I will stand, and so
shall Trinculo.

Enter ARIEL, *invisible.*

---

12. *recover,* reach
14. *standard,* ensign
15. *no standard,* i.e., incapable of standing up
16, 17. *run, lie,* (secondary meanings of) make water and excrete
17. *go,* walk
23. *case,* fit condition
24. *deboshed,* debauched
28. *natural,* fool
36. S.D. *invisible,* ('a robe for to go invisible' is listed in an Elizabethan stage
account)

CALIBAN. As I told thee before, I am subject to a tyrant,
    A sorcerer, that by his cunning hath
    Cheated me of the island.
ARIEL. Thou liest.
CALIBAN.   Thou liest, thou jesting monkey thou!   40
    I would my valiant master would destroy thee.
    I do not lie.
STEPHANO. Trinculo, if you trouble him any more in's tale,
    by this hand, I will supplant some of your teeth.
TRINCULO. Why, I said nothing.
STEPHANO. Mum then, and no more.—Proceed.
CALIBAN. I say by sorcery he got this isle;
    From me he got it. If thy greatness will
    Revenge it on him—for I know thou dar'st,
    But this thing dare not—   50
STEPHANO. That's most certain.
CALIBAN. Thou shalt be lord of it, and I'll serve thee.
STEPHANO. How now shall this be compassed?
    Canst thou bring me to the party?
CALIBAN. Yea, yea, my lord! I'll yield him thee asleep,
    Where thou mayst knock a nail into his head.
ARIEL. Thou liest; thou canst not.
CALIBAN. What a pied ninny's this! Thou scurvy patch!
    I do beseech thy greatness give him blows
    And take his bottle from him. When that's gone,   60
    He shall drink naught but brine, for I'll not show him
    Where the quick freshes are.
STEPHANO. Trinculo, run into no further danger: interrupt the mon-
    ster one word further and, by this hand, I'll turn my mercy out o'
    doors and make a stockfish of thee.
TRINCULO. Why, what did I? I did nothing. I'll go farther off.
STEPHANO. Didst thou not say he lied?
ARIEL. Thou liest.
STEPHANO. Do I so? Take thou that! (*Strikes Trinculo.*) As you like
    this, give me the lie another time.   70
TRINCULO. I did not give the lie. Out o' your wits, and hearing too?
    A pox o' your bottle! This can sack and drinking do. A murrain
    on your monster, and the devil take your fingers!

---

50. *this thing*, i.e., himself (or perhaps Trinculo)
54. *party*, person
58. *pied ninny*, motley fool (Trinculo wears a jester's costume) ; *patch*, clown
62. *quick freshes*, fresh-water springs
65. *stockfish*, dried cod, prepared by beating
72. *murrain*, cattle disease

CALIBAN. Ha, ha, ha!

STEPHANO. Now forward with your tale.—Prithee stand further off.

CALIBAN. Beat him enough. After a little time
  I'll beat him too.

STEPHANO.   Stand farther.—Come, proceed.

CALIBAN. Why, as I told thee, 'tis a custom with him
  I' th' afternoon to sleep: there thou mayst brain him,
  Having first seized his books, or with a log   80
  Batter his skull, or paunch him with a stake,
  Or cut his wesand with thy knife. Remember
  First to possess his books; for without them
  He's but a sot, as I am, nor hath not
  One spirit to command. They all do hate him
  As rootedly as I. Burn but his books.
  He has brave utensils (for so he calls them)
  Which, when he has a house, he'll deck withal.
  And that most deeply to consider is
  The beauty of his daughter. He himself   90
  Calls her a nonpareil. I never saw a woman
  But only Sycorax my dam and she;
  But she as far surpasseth Sycorax
  As great'st does least.

STEPHANO.   Is it so brave a lass?

CALIBAN. Ay, lord. She will become thy bed, I warrant,
  And bring thee forth brave brood.

STEPHANO. Monster, I will kill this man: his daughter and I will be
  king and queen, save our Graces! and Trinculo and thyself shall
  be viceroys. Dost thou like the plot, Trinculo?

TRINCULO. Excellent.   100

STEPHANO. Give me thy hand. I am sorry I beat thee; but while thou
  liv'st, keep a good tongue in thy head.

CALIBAN. Within this half hour will he be asleep.
  Wilt thou destroy him then?

STEPHANO.   Ay, on mine honor.

ARIEL. This will I tell my master.

CALIBAN. Thou mak'st me merry; I am full of pleasure.
  Let us be jocund. Will you troll the catch

---

81. *paunch,* stab in the belly
82. *wesand,* windpipe
84. *sot,* fool
87. *utensils,* furnishings
107. *troll the catch,* sing the part-song

You taught me but whilere?

STEPHANO. At thy request, monster, I will do reason, any reason.
Come on, Trinculo, let us sing. *Sings.* 110

Flout 'em and scout 'em
And scout 'em and flout 'em!
Thought is free.

CALIBAN. That's not the tune.

Ariel plays the tune on a tabor and pipe.

STEPHANO. What is this same?

TRINCULO. This is the tune of our catch, played by the picture of
Nobody.

STEPHANO. If thou beest a man, show thyself in thy likeness.
If thou beest a devil, take't as thou list.

TRINCULO. O, forgive me my sins! 120

STEPHANO. He that dies pays all debts. I defy thee.
Mercy upon us!

CALIBAN. Art thou afeard?

STEPHANO. No, monster, not I.

CALIBAN. Be not afeard: the isle is full of noises,
Sounds and sweet airs that give delight and hurt not.
Sometimes a thousand twangling instruments
Will hum about mine ears; and sometimes voices
That, if I then had waked after long sleep,
Will make me sleep again; and then, in dreaming, 130
The clouds methought would open and show riches
Ready to drop upon me, that, when I waked,
I cried to dream again.

STEPHANO. This will prove a brave kingdom to me, where I shall have
my music for nothing.

CALIBAN. When Prospero is destroyed.

STEPHANO. That shall be by and by: I remember the story.

TRICULO. The sound is going away: let's follow it, and after do our
work.

STEPHANO. Lead, monster; we'll follow. I would I could see this 140
taborer: he lays it on. Wilt come?

TRINCULO. I'll follow, Stephano. *Exeunt.*

---

108. *whilere*, just now

111. *scout*, (F reads 'cout,' which may be a word meaning 'befool')

114. s.D. *tabor*, small drum worn at the side

117. *Nobody*, (referring to pictures of figures with arms and legs but no trunk, used
on signs and elsewhere)

119. *take't as thou list*, i.e., suit yourself

137. *by and by*, right away

SCENE 3

Enter ALONSO, SEBASTIAN, ANTONIO, GONZALO, ADRIAN,
FRANCISCO, &c.

GONZALO. By'r Lakin, I can go no further, sir:
  My old bones ache: here's a maze trod indeed
  Through forthrights and meanders. By your patience,
  I needs must rest me.
ALONZO.   Old lord, I cannot blame thee,
  Who am myself attached with weariness
  To th' dulling of my spirits. Sit down and rest.
  Even here I will put off my hope, and keep it
  No longer for my flatterer: he is drowned
  Whom thus we stray to find; and the sea mocks
  Our frustrate search on land. Well, let him go.   10
ANTONIO. (*aside to Sebastian*) I am right glad that he's so out of
      hope.
  Do not for one repulse forgo the purpose
  That you resolved t' effect.
SEBASTIAN.   (*aside to Antonio*) The next advantage
  Will we take throughly.
ANTONIO.   (*aside to Sebastian*) Let it be to-night;
  For, now they are oppressed with travel, they
  Will not nor cannot use such vigilance
  As when they are fresh.
SEBASTIAN.   (*aside to Antonio*) I say to-night. No more.

    Solemn and strange music; and Prospero on the top
    (invisible). Enter several strange Shapes, bringing in
    a banquet; and dance about it with gentle actions of
    salutations; and, inviting the King &c. to eat, they
    depart.

ALONSO. What harmony is this? My good friends, hark!
GONZALO. Marvellous sweet music!

---

  1. *By'r Lakin*, by our Ladykin (Virgin Mary)
  3. *forthrights*, straight paths
  5. *attached*, seized
  14. *throughly*, thoroughly
  17. s.D. *on the top*, (this may refer to an upper level of the tiring-house of the
theatre)

ALONSO. Give us kind keepers, heavens! What were these? 20
SEBASTIAN. A living drollery. Now I will believe
　That there are unicorns; that in Arabia
　There is one tree, the phoenix' throne; one phoenix
　At this hour reigning there.
ANTONIO. 　　　　　　　　I'll believe both;
　And what does else want credit, come to me,
　And I'll be sworn 'tis true. Travellers ne'er did lie,
　Though fools at home condemn 'em.
GONZALO. 　　　　　　　　　　　　If in Naples
　I should report this now, would they believe me
　If I should say I saw such islanders?
　(For certes these are people of the island) 30
　Who, though they are of monstrous shape, yet note,
　Their manners are more gentle, kind, than of
　Our human generation you shall find
　Many—nay, almost any.
PROSPERO. 　　　　　　(*aside*) Honest lord,
　Thou hast said well; for some of you there present
　Are worse than devils.
ALONSO. 　　　　　　I cannot too much muse
　Such shapes, such gesture, and such sound, expressing
　(Although they want the use of tongue) a kind
　Of excellent dumb discourse.
PROSPERO. 　　　　　　　　　(*aside*) Praise in departing.
FRANCISCO. They vanished strangely.
SEBASTIAN. 　　　　　　　　　　No matter, since 40
　They have left their viands behind; for we have stomachs.
　Will't please you taste of what is here?
ALONSO. 　　　　　　　　　　Not I.
GONZALO. Faith, sir, you need not fear. When we were boys,
　Who would believe that there were mountaineers
　Dewlapped like bulls, whose throats had hanging at 'em
　Wallets of flesh? or that there were such men
　Whose heads stood in their breasts? which now we find

---

20. *kind keepers*, guardian angels
21. *living drollery*, puppet show with live figures
25. *want credit*, lack credibility
29. *islanders*, (F reads 'Islands')
36. *muse*, wonder at
39. *Praise in departing*, save your praise for the end
45. *Dewlapped*, with skin hanging from the neck (like the goitrous Swiss 'mountaineers')
47. *in their breasts*, (an ancient travellers' tale; cf. *Othello* I, iii, 144-45)

Each putter-out of five for one will bring us
Good warrant of.
ALONSO.   I will stand to, and feed;
Although my last, no matter, since I feel   50
The best is past. Brother, my lord the Duke,
Stand to, and do as we.

> *Thunder and lightning. Enter* ARIEL, *like a harpy; claps his wings upon the table; and with a quaint device the banquet vanishes.*

ARIEL. You are three men of sin, whom destiny—
That hath to instrument this lower world
And what is in't—the never-surfeited sea
Hath caused to belch up you, and on this island,
Where man doth not inhabit, you 'mongst men
Being most unfit to live, I have made you mad;
And even with such-like valor men hang and drown
Their proper selves.
                    (*Alonso, Sebastian, &c. draw their swords.*)
            You fools: I and my fellows   60
Are ministers of Fate. The elements,
Of whom your swords are tempered, may as well
Wound the loud winds, or with bemocked-at stabs
Kill the still-closing waters, as diminish
One dowle that's in my plume. My fellow ministers
Are like invulnerable. If you could hurt,
Your swords are now too massy for your strengths
And will not be uplifted. But remember
(For that's my business to you) that you three
From Milan did supplant good Prospero;   70
Exposed unto the sea, which hath requit it,
Him and his innocent child; for which foul deed
The powers, delaying, not forgetting, have

---

48. *putter-out . . . one,* traveller depositing a sum for insurance in London, to be repaid fivefold if he returned safely and proved he had gone to his destination
52. S.D. *quaint,* ingenious
54. *to,* i.e., as its
64. *still,* constantly
65. *dowle,* fibre of featherdown
66. *like,* also
67. *massy,* massive
71. *requit,* avenged; *it,* i.e., the usurpation

Incensed the seas and shores, yea, all the creatures,
Against your peace. Thee of thy son, Alonso,
They have bereft; and do pronounce by me
Ling'ring perdition (worse than any death
Can be at once) shall step by step attend
You and your ways; whose wraths to guard you from,
Which here, in this most desolate isle, else falls   80
Upon your heads, is nothing but heart's sorrow
And a clear life ensuing.

> *He vanishes in thunder; then, to soft music, enter the
> Shapes again, and dance with mocks and mows, and
> carrying out the table.*

PROSPERO. Bravely the figure of this harpy hast thou
  Performed, my Ariel; a grace it had, devouring.
  Of my instruction hast thou nothing bated
  In what thou hadst to say. So, with good life
  And observation strange, my meaner ministers
  Their several kinds have done. My high charms work,
  And these, mine enemies, are all knit up
  In their distractions: they now are in my power;   90
  And in these fits I leave them, while I visit
  Young Ferdinand, whom they suppose is drowned,
  And his and mine loved darling.   (*Exit above.*)
GONZALO. I' th' name of something holy, sir, why stand you
  In this strange stare?
ALONSO.   O, it is monstrous, monstrous!
  Methought the billows spoke and told me of it;
  The winds did sing it to me; and the thunder,
  That deep and dreadful organ pipe, pronounced
  The name of Prosper; it did bass my trespass.
  Therefore my son i' th' ooze is bedded; and   100

---

77. *perdition,* ruin
81. *heart's sorrow,* repentance
82. *clear,* innocent; s.D. *mocks and mows,* grimaces and gestures
84. *devouring,* i.e., making the banquet disappear
85. *bated,* omitted
86. *good life,* realistic acting
87. *observation strange,* wonderfully close attention
88. *several kinds,* separate parts
94. *why,* (Gonzalo has not heard Ariel's speech)
95. *it,* i.e., my sin
99. *bass,* proclaim in deep tones (literally, provide the bass part for)

I'll seek him deeper than e'er plummet sounded
And with him there lie mudded.   *Exit.*
SEBASTIAN.   But one fiend at a time,
I'll fight their legions o'er!
ANTONIO.   I'll be thy second.
                        Exeunt (Sebastian and Antonio).
GONZALO. All three of them are desperate: their great guilt,
Like poison given to work a great time after,
Now gins to bite the spirits. I do beseech you,
That are of suppler joints, follow them swiftly
And hinder them from what this ecstasy
May now provoke them to.
ADRIAN.   Follow, I pray you.   *Exeunt omnes.*

ACT IV

SCENE 1

Enter PROSPERO, FERDINAND, *and* MIRANDA.

PROSPERO. If I have too austerely punished you,
Your compensation makes amends; for I
Have given you here a third of mine own life,
Or that for which I live; who once again
I tender to thy hand. All thy vexations
Were but my trials of thy love, and thou
Hast strangely stood the test. Here, afore heaven,
I ratify this my rich gift. O Ferdinand,
Do not smile at me that I boast her off,
For thou shalt find she will outstrip all praise   10
And make it halt behind her.
FERDINAND.   I do believe it
Against an oracle.

108. *ecstasy,* madness
3. *third,* (Prospero's love, his knowledge and his power being the other two-thirds?)
7. *strangely,* in a rare fashion
9. *boast her off,* boast about her; *off,* (F reads 'of')
11. *halt,* limp
12. *Against an oracle,* even if an oracle denied it

PROSPERO. Then, as my gift, and thine own acquisition
   Worthily purchased, take my daughter. But
   If thou dost break her virgin-knot before
   All sanctimonious ceremonies may
   With full and holy rite be minist'red,
   No sweet aspersion shall the heavens let fall
   To make this contract grow; but barren hate,
   Sour-eyed disdain, and discord shall bestrew   20
   The union of your bed with weeds so loathly
   That you shall hate it both. Therefore take heed,
   As Hymen's lamp shall light you.
FERDINAND.   As I hope
   For quiet days, fair issue, and long life,
   With such love as 'tis now, the murkiest den,
   The most opportune place, the strong'st suggestion
   Our worser genius can, shall never melt
   Mine honor into lust, to take away
   The edge of that day's celebration
   When I shall think or Phoebus' steeds are foundered   30
   Or Night kept chained below.
PROSPERO.   Fairly spoke.
   Sit then and talk with her; she is thine own.
   What Ariel! my industrious servant, Ariel!

Enter ARIEL.

ARIEL. What would my potent master? Here I am.
PROSPERO. Thou and thy meaner fellows your last service
   Did worthily perform; and I must use you
   In such another trick. Go bring the rabble,
   O'er whom I give thee pow'r, here to this place.
   Incite them to quick motion; for I must
   Bestow upon the eyes of this young couple   40
   Some vanity of mine art: it is my promise,

13. *gift,* (F reads 'guest')
16. *sanctimonious,* holy
18. *aspersion,* blessing, like rain on crops
19. *grow,* become fruitful
26. *opportune,* (accent second syllable)
27. *worser genius can,* bad angel can make
30. *or . . . foundered,* either the sun-god's horses are lame
37. *rabble,* rank and file
41. *vanity,* show

And they expect it from me.

ARIEL.   Presently?

PROSPERO. Ay, with a twink.

ARIEL. Before you can 'Come' and 'Go,'
  And breathe twice and cry, 'So, so,'
  Each one, tripping on his toe,
  Will be here with mop and mow.
  Do you love me, master? No?

PROSPERO. Dearly, my delicate Ariel. Do not approach
  Till thou dost hear me call.

ARIEL.   Well: I conceive.   *Exit.*   50

PROSPERO. Look thou be true: do not give dalliance
  Too much the rein: the strongest oaths are straw
  To th' fire i' th' blood. Be more abstemious,
  Or else good night your vow!

FERDINAND.   I warrant you, sir.
  The white cold virgin snow upon my heart
  Abates the ardor of my liver.

PROSPERO.   Well.
  Now come, my Ariel: bring a corollary
  Rather than want a spirit. Appear, and pertly!
  No tongue! All eyes! Be silent.   *Soft music.*

Enter IRIS.

IRIS. Ceres, most bounteous lady, thy rich leas   60
  Of wheat, rye, barley, fetches, oats, and pease;
  Thy turfy mountains, where live nibbling sheep,
  And flat meads thatched with stover, them to keep;
  Thy banks with pionèd and twillèd brims,
  Which spongy April at thy hest betrims
  To make cold nymphs chaste crowns; and thy broom groves,

---

47. *mop and mow*, antics and gestures
50. *conceive*, understand
51. *be true*, (Prospero appears to have caught the lovers in an embrace)
56. *liver*, (supposed seat of sexual passion)
57. *corollary*, surplus
58. *want*, lack; *pertly*, briskly
60. *Iris*, goddess of the rainbow and female messenger of the gods
61. *fetches*, vetch
63. *stover*, winter food for stock
64. *pionèd and twillèd*, dug under by the current and protected by woven layers of branches (sometimes emended to 'peonied and lilied')
66. *broom groves*, clumps of gorse

Whose shadow the dismissèd bachelor loves,
Being lasslorn; thy pole-clipt vineyard;
And thy sea-marge, sterile and rocky-hard,
Where thou thyself dost air—the queen o' th' sky,   70
Whose wat'ry arch and messenger am I,
Bids thee leave these, and with her sovereign grace,
Here on this grass-plot, in this very place,
To come and sport: her peacocks fly amain.
Approach, rich Ceres, her to entertain.

Enter CERES.

CERES. Hail, many-colorèd messenger, that ne'er
  Dost disobey the wife of Jupiter,
  Who, with thy saffron wings, upon my flow'rs
  Diffusest honey drops, refreshing show'rs,
  And with each end of thy blue bow dost crown   80
  My bosky acres and my unshrubbed down,
  Rich scarf to my proud earth—why hath thy queen
  Summoned me hither to this short-grassed green?
Iris. A contract of true love to celebrate
  And some donation freely to estate
  On the blessed lovers.
CERES.   Tell me, heavenly bow,
  If Venus or her son, as thou dost know,
  Do now attend the queen? Since they did plot
  The means that dusky Dis my daughter got,
  Her and her blind boy's scandalled company   90
  I have forsworn.
IRIS.   Of her society
  Be not afraid: I met her Deity
  Cutting the clouds towards Paphos, and her son

---

68. *pole-clipt*, pruned; *vineyard* (probably a trisyllable)
69. *sea-marge*, shore
70. *queen*, i.e., Juno
74. *peacocks*, (these were sacred to Juno, as doves were to Venus [l. 94], and drew her chariot)
81. *bosky*, wooded
85. *estate*, bestow
87. *her son*, Cupid, often represented as blind or blindfolded
89. *means*, i.e., the abduction of Proserpine, Ceres's daughter, by Pluto (Dis), god of the lower ('dusky') world
90. *scandalled*, disgraceful
92. *her Deity*, i.e., her Divine Majesty
93. *Paphos*, (in Cyprus, center of Venus's cult)

Dove-drawn with her. Here thought they to have done
Some wanton charm upon this man and maid,
Whose vows are, that no bed-right shall be paid
Till Hymen's torch be lighted; but in vain.
Mar's hot minion is returned again;
Her waspish-headed son has broke his arrows,
Swears he will shoot no more, but play with sparrows   100
And be a boy right out.

Enter JUNO.

CERES.   Highest queen of state,
    Great Juno, comes; I know her by her gait.
JUNO. How does my bounteous sister? Go with me
    To bless this twain, that they may prosperous be
    And honored in their issue.

They sing.

JUNO.   Honor, riches, marriage blessing,
         Long continuance, and increasing,
         Hourly joys be still upon you!
         Juno sings her blessings on you.
CERES.   Earth's increase, foison plenty,   110
         Barns and garners never empty,
         Vines with clust'ring bunches growing,
         Plants with goodly burden bowing;
         Spring come to you at the farthest
         In the very end of harvest.
         Scarcity and want shall shun you,
         Ceres' blessing so is on you.
FERDINAND. This is a most majestic vision, and
    Harmonious charmingly. May I be bold
    To think these spirits?
PROSPERO.   Spirits, which by mine art   120
    I have from their confines called to enact
    My present fancies.

---

98. *Mars's . . . again*, the lustful mistress of Mars (Venus) has gone back to where
she came from
99. *waspish-headed*, spiteful and inclined to sting (with his arrows)
101. *right out*, outright
108. *still*, constantly
110. *foison*, abundance

FERDINAND.   Let me live here ever!
 So rare a wond'red father and a wise
 Makes this place Paradise.
    Juno and Ceres whisper, and send Iris on employment.
PROSPERO.   Sweet, now, silence!
 Juno and Ceres whisper seriously.
 There's something else to do. Hush and be mute,
 Or else our spell is marred.
IRIS. You nymphs, called Naiades, of the windring brooks,
 With your sedged crowns and ever-harmless looks,
 Leave your crisp channels, and on this green land   130
 Answer your summons; Juno does command.
 Come, temperate nymphs, and help to celebrate
 A contract of true love: be not too late.

     Enter certain Nymphs.

 You sunburned sicklemen, of August weary,
 Come hither from the furrow and be merry.
 Make holiday: your rye-straw hats put on,
 And these fresh nymphs encounter every one
 In country footing.

   Enter certain REAPERS, *properly habited. They join with
   the Nymphs in a graceful dance; towards the end whereof
   Prospero starts suddenly and speaks; after which, to a
   strange, hollow, and confused noise, they heavily vanish.*

PROSPERO. (*aside*) I had forgot that foul conspiracy
 Of the beast Caliban and his confederates   140
 Against my life: the minute of their plot
 Is almost come. (*to the Spirits*) Well done! Avoid! No more!
FERDINAND. This is strange. Your father's in some passion
 That works him strongly.
MIRANDA.   Never till this day
 Saw I him touched with anger so distempered.
PROSPERO. You do look, my son, in a moved sort,

---

 123. *wond'red*, wonderful; *wise*, (some copies of F read 'wife')
 128. *windring*, winding and wandering
 130. *crisp*, rippling
 138. s.D. *speaks*, (thereby dissolving the scene, which depended on silence)
 142. *Avoid*, be off
 146. *moved sort*, troubled state

As if you were dismayed: be cheerful, sir.
Our revels now are ended. These our actors,
As I foretold you, were all spirits and
Are melted into air, into thin air;   150
And, like the baseless fabric of this vision,
The cloud-capped towers, the gorgeous palaces,
The solemn temples, the great globe itself,
Yea, all which it inherit, shall dissolve,
And, like this insubstantial pageant faded,
Leave not a rack behind. We are such stuff
As dreams are made on, and our little life
Is rounded with a sleep. Sir, I am vexed.
Bear with my weakness: my old brain is troubled.
Be not disturbed with my infirmity.   160
If you be pleased, retire into my cell
And there repose. A turn or two I'll walk
To still my beating mind.
FERDINAND, MIRANDA.   We wish your peace.
                    Exit (Ferdinand with Miranda).

                    Enter ARIEL.

PROSPERO. Come with a thought! I thank thee, Ariel. Come.
ARIEL. Thy thoughts I cleave to. What's thy pleasure?
PROSPERO.   Spirit,
    We must prepare to meet with Caliban.
ARIEL. Ay, my commander: when I presented Ceres,
    I thought to have told thee of it, but I feared
    Lest I might anger thee.
PROSPERO. Say again, where didst thou leave these varlets?   170
ARIEL. I told you, sir, they were redhot with drinking;
    So full of valor that they smote the air
    For breathing in their faces, beat the ground
    For kissing of their feet; yet always bending
    Towards their project. Then I beat my tabor;

---

148. *revels*, pageants
151. *baseless*, insubstantial, non-material
154. *it inherit*, occupy it
156. *rack*, wisp of cloud
157. *on*, of
167. *presented*, acted the part of (?) introduced (?)
170. *varlets*, ruffians

At which like unbacked colts they pricked their ears,
Advanced their eyelids, lifted up their noses
As they smelt music. So I charmed their ears
That calf-like they my lowing followed through
Toothed briers, sharp furzes, pricking goss, and thorns,   180
Which ent'red their frail shins. At last I left them
I' th' filthy mantled pool beyond your cell,
There dancing up to th' chins, that the foul lake
O'erstunk their feet.
PROSPERO.   This was well done, my bird.
Thy shape invisible retain thou still.
The trumpery in my house, go bring it hither
For stale to catch these thieves.
ARIEL.   I go, I go.   *Exit.*
PROSPERO. A devil, a born devil, on whose nature
Nurture can never stick: on whom my pains,
Humanely taken, all, all lost, quite lost!   190
And as with age his body uglier grows,
So his mind cankers. I will plague them all,
Even to roaring.

Enter ARIEL, *loaden with glistering apparel, &c.*

Come, hang them on this line.

(PROSPERO *and* ARIEL *remain, invisible.*) *Enter* CALIBAN,
STEPHANO, *and* TRINCULO, *all wet.*

CALIBAN. Pray you tread softly, that the blind mole may not
Hear a foot fall. We now are near his cell.
STEPHANO. Monster, your fairy, which you say is a harmless fairy,
has done little better than played the Jack with us.
TRINCULO. Monster, I do smell all horse-piss, at which my nose is in
great indignation.

---

176. *unbacked,* unbroken
177. *Advanced,* lifted up
180. *goss,* gorse
182. *mantled,* scummed
187. *stale,* decoy
192. *cankers,* festers
193. *line,* lime or linden-tree, or perhaps a clothesline made of hair
197. *Jack,* (1) knave (2) jack-o'-lantern, will-o'-the-wisp

STEPHANO. So is mine. Do you hear, monster? If I should take a   200
displeasure against you, look you—

TRINCULO. Thou wert but a lost monster.

CALIBAN. Good my lord, give me thy favor still.
Be patient, for the prize I'll bring thee to
Shall hoodwink this mischance. Therefore speak softly.
All's hushed as midnight yet.

TRINCULO. Ay, but to lose our bottles in the pool—

STEPHANO. There is not only disgrace and dishonor in that, monster,
but an infinite loss.

TRINCULO. There's more to me than my wetting. Yet this is your   210
harmless fairy, monster.

STEPHANO. I will fetch my bottle, though I be o'er ears for my labor.

CALIBAN. Prithee, my king, be quiet. Seest thou here?
This is the mouth o' th' cell. No noise, and enter.
Do that good mischief which may make this island
Thine own for ever, and I, thy Caliban,
For aye thy foot-licker.

STEPHANO. Give me thy hand. I do begin to have bloody
thoughts.

TRINCULO. O King Stephano! O peer! O worthy Stephano, look   220
what a wardrobe here is for thee!

CALIBAN. Let it alone, thou fool! It is but trash.

TRINCULO. O, ho, monster! we know what belongs to a frippery. O
King Stephano!

STEPHANO. Put off that gown, Trinculo: by this hand, I'll have
that gown!

TRINCULO. Thy Grace shall have it.

CALIBAN. The dropsy drown this fool! What do you mean
To dote thus on such luggage? Let't alone,
And do the murder first. If he awake,   230
From toe to crown he'll fill our skins with pinches,
Make us strange stuff.

STEPHANO. Be you quiet, monster. Mistress line, is not this my jerkin? (*Takes it down.*) Now is the jerkin under the line. Now, jerkin,

---

205. *hoodwink*, cover over

220. *peer*, (referring to the song 'King Stephen was a worthy peer,' quoted in
Othello II, iii, 84–91)

223. *frippery*, old-clothes shop

229. *luggage*, junk

233. ff. (the jokes are probably obscene, but their point is lost; sailors crossing the
'line' or equator proverbially lost their hair from scurvy)

you are like to lose your hair and prove a bald jerkin.

TRINCULO. Do, do! We steal by line and level, an't like your Grace.

STEPHANO. I thank thee for that jest. Here's a garment for't. Wit shall not go unrewarded while I am king of this country. 'Steal by line ank level' is an excellent pass of pate. There's another garment for't.   240

TRINCULO. Monster, come put some lime upon your fingers, and away with the rest.

CALIBAN. I will have none on't. We shall lose our time
And all be turned to barnacles, or to apes
With foreheads villainous low.

STEPHANO. Monster, lay-to your fingers: help to bear this away where my hogshead of wine is, or I'll turn you out of my kingdom. Go to, carry this.

TRINCULO. And this.

STEPHANO. Ay, and this.   250

A noise of hunters heard. Enter divers Spirits in shape of dogs and hounds, hunting them about, Prospero and Ariel setting them on.

PROSPERO. Hey, Mountain, hey!

ARIEL. Silver! there it goes, Silver!

PROSPERO. Fury, Fury! There, Tyrant, there! Hark, hark!
        (*Caliban, Stephano, and Trinculo are driven out.*)
Go, charge my goblins that they grind their joints
With dry convulsions, shorten up their sinews
With agèd cramps, and more pinch-spotted make them
Than pard or cat o' mountain.

ARIEL.   Hark, they roar!

PROSPERO. Let them be hunted soundly. At this hour
Lie at my mercy all mine enemies.
Shortly shall all my labors end, and thou   260
Shalt have the air at freedom. For a little,
Follow, and do me service.   *Exeunt.*

---

236. *by line and level*, according to rule (with pun on 'line') ; *an't like*, if it please
239. *pass of pate*, sally of wit
241. *lime*, birdlime (sticky, hence appropriate for stealing)
244. *barnacles*, geese
255. *dry*, (resulting from deficiency of 'humors' or bodily liquids)
256. *aged*, i.e., such as old people have
257. *pard or cat o' mountain*, leopard or catamount

ACT V

SCENE 1

Enter PROSPERO *in his magic robes, and* ARIEL.

PROSPERO. Now does my project gather to a head.
My charms crack not, my spirits obey, and time
Goes upright with his carriage. How's the day?
ARIEL. On the sixth hour, at which time, my lord,
You said our work should cease.
PROSPERO.   I did say so
When first I raised the tempest. Say, my spirit,
How fares the King and 's followers?
ARIEL.   Confined together
In the same fashion as you gave in charge,
Just as you left them—all prisoners, sir,
In the line grove which weather-fends your cell.   10
They cannot budge till your release. The King,
His brother, and yours abide all three distracted,
And the remainder mourning over them,
Brimful of sorrow and dismay; but chiefly
Him that you termed, sir, the good old Lord Gonzalo.
His tears run down his beard like winter's drops
From eaves of reeds. Your charms so strongly works 'em,
That if you now beheld them, your affections
Would become tender.
PROSPERO.   Dost thou think so, spirit?
ARIEL. Mine would, sir, were I human.
PROSPERO.   And mine shall.   20
Hast thou, which art but air, a touch, a feeling
Of their afflictions, and shall not myself,
One of their kind, that relish all as sharply
Passion as they, be kindlier moved than thou art?
Though with their high wrongs I am struck to th' quick,

2–3. *time . . . carriage,* time's burden is light
10. *weather-fends,* protects from the weather
11. *till your release,* until you release them
17. *eaves of reeds,* i.e., a thatched roof
23. *relish,* feel; *all,* quite

Yet with my nobler reason 'gainst my fury
Do I take part. The rarer action is
In virtue than in vengeance. They being penitent,
The sole drift of my purpose doth extend
Not a frown further. Go, release them, Ariel. 30
My charms I'll break, their senses I'll restore,
And they shall be themselves.
ARIEL.   I'll fetch them, sir.   *Exit.*
PROSPERO. Ye elves of hills, brooks, standing lakes, and groves,
    And ye that on the sands with printless foot
    Do chase the ebbing Neptune, and do fly him
    When he comes back; you demi-puppets that
    By moonshine do the green sour ringlets make,
    Whereof the ewe not bites; and you whose pastime
    Is to make midnight mushrumps, that rejoice
    To hear the solemn curfew; by whose aid 40
    (Weak masters though ye be) I have bedimmed
    The noontide sun, called forth the mutinous winds,
    And 'twixt the green sea and the azured vault
    Set roaring war; to the dread rattling thunder
    Have I given fire and rifted Jove's stout oak
    With his own bolt; the strong-based promontory
    Have I made shake and by the spurs plucked up
    The pine and cedar; graves at my command
    Have waked their sleepers, oped, and let 'em forth
    By my so potent art. But this rough magic 50
    I here abjure; and when I have required
    Some heavenly music (which even now I do)
    To work mine end upon their senses that
    This airy charm is for, I'll break my staff,
    Bury it certain fathoms in the earth,
    And deeper than did ever plummet sound
    I'll drown my book.   *Solemn music.*

Here enters ARIEL *before; then* ALONSO, *with a frantic
    gesture, attended by* GONZALO; SEBASTIAN *and* ANTONIO

---

36. *demi-puppets,* i.e., fairies
39. *mushrumps,* mushrooms
41. *masters,* forces
45. *rifted,* split
47. *spurs,* roots
51. *required,* asked for
53. *their senses that,* the senses of those whom

in like manner, attended by ADRIAN *and* FRANCISCO.
*They all enter the circle which Prospero has made, and
there stand charmed; which Prospero observing,
speaks.*

A solemn air, and the best comforter
To an unsettled fancy, cure thy brains,
Now useless, boiled within thy skull! There stand,   60
For you are spell-stopped.
Holy Gonzalo, honorable man,
Mine eyes, ev'n sociable to the show of thine,
Fall fellowly drops. The charm dissolves space;
And as the morning steals upon the night,
Melting the darkness, so their rising senses
Begin to chase the ignorant fumes that mantle
Their clearer reason. O good Gonzalo,
My true preserver, and a loyal sir
To him thou folow'st, I will pay thy graces   70
Home both in word and deed. Most cruelly
Didst thou, Alonso, use me and my daughter.
Thy brother was a furtherer in the act.
Thou art pinched for't now, Sebastian. Flesh and blood,
You, brother mine, that entertained ambition,
Expelled remorse and nature; who, with Sebastian
(Whose inward pinches therefore are most strong),
Would here have killed your king, I do forgive thee,
Unnatural though thou art. Their understanding
Begins to swell, and the approaching tide   80
Will shortly fill the reasonable shore,
That now lies foul and muddy. Not one of them
That yet looks on me or would know me. Ariel,
Fetch me the hat and rapier in my cell.
I will discase me, and myself present
As I was sometime Milan. Quickly, spirit!
Thou shalt ere long be free.

(*Exit Ariel and returns immediately.*)

---

58. *and,* i.e., which is
63. *sociable,* sympathetic; *show,* sight
64. *Fall,* let fall
70. *graces,* favors
76. *remorse,* pity; *nature,* natural feeling
85. *discase,* undress
86. *sometime Milan,* when I was Duke of Milan

Ariel sings and helps to attire him.

Where the bee sucks, there suck I;
In a cowslip's bell I lie;
There I couch when owls do cry.   90
On the bat's back I do fly
After summer merrily.
  Merrily, merrily shall I live now
Under the blossom that hangs on the bough.
PROSPERO. Why, that's my dainty Ariel! I shall miss thee,
  But yet thou shalt have fredom; so, so, so.
To the King's ship, invisible as thou art!
There shalt thou find the mariners asleep
Under the hatches. The master and the boatswain
Being awake, enforce them to this place,   100
And presently, I prithee.
ARIEL. I drink the air before me, and return
  Or ere your pulse twice beat.   *Exit.*
GONZALO. All torment, trouble, wonder, and amazement
  Inhabits here. Some heavenly power guide us
Out of this fearful country!
PROSPERO.   Behold, sir King,
  The wrongèd Duke of Milan, Prospero,
For more assurance that a living prince
Does now speak to thee, I embrace thy body,
And to thee and thy company I bid   110
A hearty welcome.
ALONSO.   Whe'r thou be'st he or no,
  Or some enchanted trifle to abuse me,
As late I have been, I not know. Thy pulse
Beats, as of flesh and blood; and, since I saw thee,
Th' affliction of my mind amends, with which,
I fear, a madness held me. This must crave
(An if this be at all) a most strange story.
Thy dukedom I resign and do entreat
Thou pardon me my wrongs. But how should Prospero

---

101. *presently*, right away
102. *drink the air*, i.e., consume space
112. *trifle*, trick; *abuse*, deceive
116. *crave*, require
117. *And if . . . all*, if this is really happening

Be living and be here?
PROSPERO.   First, noble friend,   120
Let me embrace thine age, whose honor cannot
Be measured or confined.
GONZALO.   Whether this be
Or be not, I'll not swear.
PROSPERO.   You do yet taste
Some subtleties o' th' isle, that will not let you
Believe things certain. Welcome, my friends all.
(*Aside to Sebastian and Antonio*) But you, my brace of lords,
     were I so minded,
I here could pluck his Highness' frown upon you,
And justify you traitors. At this time
I will tell no tales.
SEBASTIAN.   (*aside*) The devil speaks in him.
PROSPERO.   No.
For you, most wicked sir, whom to call brother   130
Would even infect my mouth, I do forgive
Thy rankest fault—all of them; and require
My dukedom of thee, which perforce I know
Thou must restore.
ALONSO.   If thou beest Prospero,
Give us particulars of thy preservation;
How thou hast met us here, who three hours since
Were wracked upon this shore; where I have lost
(How sharp the point of this remembrance is!)
My dear son Ferdinand.
PROSPERO.   I am woe for't, sir.
ALONSO. Irreparable is the loss, and patience   140
Says it is past her cure.
PROSPERO.   I rather think
You have not sought her help, of whose soft grace
For the like loss I have her sovereign aid
And rest myself content.
ALONSO.   You the like loss?
PROSPERO. As great to me as late; and, supportable

---

124. *subtleties*, (secondary meaning of) elaborate pastries representing allegorical figures, used in banquets and pageants
127. *pluck*, pull down
128. *justify*, prove
139. *woe*, sorry
145. *late*, recent

To make the dear loss, have I means much weaker
Than you may call to comfort you; for I
Have lost my daughter.
ALONSO.   A daughter?
O heavens, that they were living both in Naples,
The King and Queen there! That they were, I wish   150
Myself were mudded in that oozy bed
Where my son lies. When did you lose your daughter?
PROSPERO. In this last tempest. I perceive these lords
At this encounter do so much admire
That they devour their reason, and scarce think
Their eyes do offices of truth, their words
Are natural breath. But, howsoev'r you have
Been justled from your senses, know for certain
That I am Prospero, and that very duke
Which was thrust forth of Milan, who most strangely   160
Upon this shore, where you were wracked, was landed
To be the lord on't. No more yet of this;
For 'tis a chronicle of day by day,
Not a relation for a breakfast, nor
Befitting this first meeting. Welcome, sir;
This cell's my court. Here have I few attendants,
And subjects none abroad. Pray you look in.
My dukedom since you have given me again,
I will requite you with as good a thing,
At least bring forth a wonder to content ye   170
As much as me my dukedom.

Here Prospero discovers Ferdinand and Miranda playing at chess.

MIRANDA. Sweet lord, you play me false.
FERDINAND.   No, my dearest love,
I would not for the world.
MIRANDA. Yes, for a score of kingdoms you should wrangle,
And I would call it fair play.
ALONSO.   If this prove
A vision of the island, one dear son

---

146. *dear*, grievous
154. *admire*, wonder
156. *do offices*, perform services
171. S.D. *discovers*, discloses
174. *should wrangle*, i.e., playing fair, as Ferdinand is doing, is not a test of Miranda's love for him

Shall I twice lose.

SEBASTIAN. A most high miracle!

FERDINAND. Though the seas threaten, they are merciful.
  I have cursed them without cause   (*Kneels.*)

ALONSO.   Now all the blessings
  Of a glad father compass thee about!   180
  Arise, and say how thou cam'st here.

MIRANDA.   O, wonder!
  How many goodly creatures are there here!
  How beauteous mankind is! O brave new world
  That has such people in't!

PROSPERO.   'Tis new to thee.

ALONSO. What is this maid with whom thou wast at play?
  Your eld'st acquaintance cannot be three hours.
  Is she the goddess that hath severed us
  And brought us thus together?

FERDINAND.   Sir, she is mortal;
  But by immortal providence she's mine.
  I chose her when I could not ask my father   190
  For his advice, nor thought I had one. She
  Is daughter to this famous Duke of Milan,
  Of whom so often I have heard renown
  But never saw before; of whom I have
  Received a second life; and second father
  This lady makes him to me.

ALONSO.   I am hers.
  But, O, how oddly will it sound that I
  Must ask my child forgiveness!

PROSPERO.   There, sir, stop.
  Let us not burden our remembrance with
  A heaviness that's gone.

GONZALO.   I have inly wept,   200
  Or should have spoke ere this. Look down, you gods,
  And on this couple drop a blessèd crown!
  For it is you that have chalked forth the way
  Which brought us hither.

ALONSO.   I say amen, Gonzalo.

GONZALO. Was Milan thrust from Milan that his issue
  Should become kings of Naples? O, rejoice
  Beyond a common joy, and set it down

---

186. *eld'st*, i.e., longest period of

With gold on lasting pillars: in one voyage
Did Claribel her husband find at Tunis,
And Ferdinand her brother found a wife   210
Where he himself was lost; Prospero his dukedom
In a poor isle; and all of us ourselves
When no man was his own.
ALONSO.   (*to Ferdinand and Miranda*) Give me your hands.
Let grief and sorrow still embrace his heart
That doth not wish you joy.
GONZALO.   Be it so! Amen!

Enter ARIEL, *with the* MASTER *and* BOATSWAIN *amazedly following.*

O, look, sir; look sir! Here is more of us!
I prophesied, if a gallows were on land,
This fellow could not drown. Now, blasphemy,
That swear'st grace o'erboard, not an oath on shore?
Has thou no mouth by land? What is the news?   220
BOATSWAIN. The best news is that we have safely found
Our king and company; the next, our ship,
Which, but three glasses since, we gave out split,
Is tight and yare and bravely rigged as when
We first put out to sea.
ARIEL.   (*aside to Prospero*) Sir, all this service
Have I done since I went.
PROSPERO.   (*aside to Ariel*) My tricksy spirit!
ALONSO. These are not natural events; they strengthen
From strange to stranger. Say, how came you hither?
BOATSWAIN. If I did think, sir, I were well awake,
I'ld strive to tell you. We were dead of sleep   230
And (how we know not) all clapped under hatches;
Where, but even now, with strange and several noises
Of roaring, shrieking, howling, jingling chains,
And moe diversity of sounds, all horrible,
We were awaked; straightway at liberty;
Where we, in all her trim, freshly beheld

---

214. *still*, forever
224. *yare*, shipshape
226. *tricksy*, i.e., ingenious
232. *several*, various
234. *moe*, more
236. *trim*, sail

Our royal, good, and gallant ship, our master
Cap'ring to eye her. On a trice, so please you,
Even in a dream, were we divided from them
And were brought moping hither.

ARIEL. (*aside to Prospero*) Was't well done? 240
PROSPERO. (*aside to Ariel*) Bravely, my diligence. Thou shalt be free.
ALONSO. This is as strange a maze as e'er men trod,
    And there is in this business more than nature
    Was ever conduct of. Some oracle
    Must rectify our knowledge.
PROSPERO.   Sir, my liege,
    Do not infest your mind with beating on
    The strangeness of this business: at picked leisure,
    Which shall be shortly, single I'll resolve you
    (Which to you shall seem probable) of every
    These happened accidents; till when, be cheerful 250
    And think of each thing well. (*aside to Ariel*) Come hither, spirit.
    Set Caliban and his companions free.
    Untie the spell. (*Exit Ariel.*) How fares my gracious sir?
    There are yet missing of your company
    Some few odd lads that you remember not.

> *Enter* ARIEL, *driving in* CALIBAN, STEPHANO, *and* TRIN-
> CULO, *in their stolen apparel.*

STEPHANO. Every man shift for all the rest, and let no man take care
    for himself; for all is but fortune. Coragio, bully-monster, cora-
    gio!
TRINCULO. If these be true spies which I wear in my head, here's
    a goodly sight. 260
CALIBAN. O Setebos, these be brave spirits indeed!
    How fine my master is! I am afraid
    He will chastise me.
SEBASTIAN.   Ha, ha!
    What things are these, my Lord Antonio?
    Will money buy 'em?

---

238. *Cap'ring*, dancing for joy; *eye*, see
240. *moping*, in a daze
244. *conduct*, conductor
246. *infest*, tease
248. *single*, privately; *resolve*, explain
249. *every*, every one of
250. *accidents*, incidents
259. *spies*, eyes

ANTONIO.   Very like. One of them
  Is a plain fish and no doubt marketable.
PROSPERO. Mark but the badges of these men, my lords,
  Then say if they be true. This misshapen knave,
  His mother was a witch, and one so strong
  That could control the moon, make flows and ebbs,   270
  And deal in her command without her power.
  These three have robbed me, and this demi-devil
  (For he's a bastard one) had plotted with them
  To take my life. Two of these fellows you
  Must know and own; this thing of darkness I
  Acknowledge mine.
CALIBAN.   I shall be pinched to death.
ALONSO. Is not this Stephano, my drunken butler?
SEBASTIAN. He is drunk now: where had he wine?
ALONSO. And Trinculo is reeling ripe: where should they
  Find this grand liquor that hath gilded 'em?   280
  How cam'st thou in this pickle?
TRINCULO. I have been in such a pickle, since I saw you last, that
  I fear me will never out of my bones. I shall not fear fly-blowing.
SEBASTIAN. Why, how now, Stephano?
STEPHANO. O, touch me not! I am not Stephano, but a cramp.
PROSPERO. You'ld be king o' the isle, sirrah?
STEPHANO. I should have been a sore one then.
ALONSO. This is a strange thing as e'er I looked on.
PROSPERO. He is as disproportioned in his manners
  As in his shape. Go, sirrah, to my cell;   290
  Take with you your companions. As you look
  To have my pardon, trim it handsomely.
CALIBAN. Ay, that I will; and I'll be wise hereafter,
  And seek for grace. What a thrice-double ass
  Was I to take this drunkard for a god
  And worship this dull fool!
PROSPERO.   Go to! Away!
ALONSO. Hence and bestow your luggage where you found it.
SEBASTIAN. Or stole it rather.
              (*Exeunt Caliban, Stephano, and Trinculo.*)

---

267. *badges of these men*, signs of these servants
268. *true*, honest
271. *her*, i.e., the moon's; *without*, beyond
282. *pickle*, (1) predicament (2) preservative (from the horsepond; hence insects
will let him alone)
285. *Stephano*, (this name is said to be a slang Neapolitan term for stomach)
287. *sore*, (1) tyrannical (2) aching

PROSPERO. Sir, I invite your Highness and your train
  To my poor cell, where you shall take your rest   300
  For this one night; which part of it, I'll waste
  With such discourse as, I not doubt, shall make it
  Go quick away—the story of my life,
  And the particular accidents gone by
  Since I came to this isle; and in the morn
  I'll bring you to your ship, and so to Naples,
  Where I have hope to see the nuptial
  Of these our dear-beloved solemnizèd;
  And thence retire me to my Milan, where
  Every third thought shall be my grave.
ALONSO.   I long   310
  To hear the story of your life, which must
  Take the ear strangely.
PROSPERO.   I'll deliver all;
  And promise you calm seas, auspicious gales,
  And sail so expeditious that shall catch
  Your royal fleet far off.—My Ariel, chick,
  That is thy charge. Then to the elements
  Be free and fare thou well!—Please you draw near.

                                 Exeunt omnes.

EPILOGUE,

spoken by Prospero.

Now my charms are all o'erthrown,
And what strength I have's mine own,
Which is most faint. Now 'tis true
I must be here confined by you,
Or sent to Naples. Let me not,
Since I have my dukedom got
And pardoned the deceiver, dwell
In this bare island by your spell;
But release me from my bands
With the help of your good hands.   10

301. *waste*, spend
308. *solemnizèd*, (accent second syllable)
312. *Take*, captivate; *deliver*, tell
314. *sail*, sailing
8. *spell*, i.e., silence
9. *bands*, bonds
10. *hands*, i.e., applause to break the spell

Gentle breath of yours my sails
Must fill, or else my project fails,
Which was to please. Now I want
Spirits to enforce, art to enchant;
And my ending is despair
Unless I be relieved by prayer,
Which pierces so that it assaults
Mercy itself and frees all faults.
As you from crimes would pardoned be,
Let your indulgence set me free.   *Exit.*   20

Questions for Discussion

1. In what respect is the action of *The Tempest* similar to that of a tragedy? In particular what are its similarities to *King Lear?* In this connection consider Lear and Prospero, Miranda and Cordelia, Edmund and Antonio as well as the storm in each play. In what respect does the play resemble a comedy or tragicomedy ("the happy shipwreck")?

2. What are the three plots in the play and how are they related in terms of theme? Why are they appropriate to romance?

3. How does Miranda mature? What part do Prospero and Ferdinand play in her awakening to maturity?

4. How is Gonzalo's reaction to being shipwrecked on the island different from the others in the group?

5. Why does Prospero forgive his enemies at the end of the play? Is this consistent with his character?

6. To what extent is Antonio the moving spirit behind the evil in the play? Why is he never reconciled with his brother at the end of the play?

7. *The Tempest* has been interpreted as illustrating love, liberty, and wonder in opposition to lust, license, and banality. Justify this interpretation by reference to events and characters.

8. One critic believes that the theme of the play is the "opposition between the worlds of Prospero's Art, and Caliban's Nature." How true is this? In your opinion is Caliban "the core of the play"?

9. Although the play is set on a remote island and is filled with magic, is there any evidence of its being seriously concerned with human existence here and now?

10. To what extent does the development of the play follow the structure indicated in the Introduction?

---

13. *want,* lack

Samuel Taylor Coleridge (1772–1834)

The Rime of the Ancient Mariner

Argument

How a Ship, having first sailed to the Equator, was driven by Storms to the cold Country towards the South Pole; how the Ancient Mariner cruelly and in contempt of the laws of hospitality killed a Seabird and how he was followed by many and strange Judgements: and in what manner he came back to his own Country.

PART I

An ancient Mariner meeteth three Gallants bidden to a wedding-feast, and detaineth one.

It is an ancient Mariner,
And he stoppeth one of three.
"By thy long grey beard and glittering eye,
Now wherefore stopp'st thou me?

The Bridegroom's doors are opened wide,
And I am next of kin;
The guests are met, the feast is set:
May'st hear the merry din."

He holds him with his skinny hand,
"There was a ship," quoth he.   10
"Hold off! Unhand me, gray-beard loon!"
Eftsoons[1] his hand dropt he.

The Wedding-Guest is spellbound by the eye of the old sea-faring man, and constrained to hear his tale.

He holds him with his glittering eye—
The Wedding-Guest stood still,
And listens like a three years' child:
The Mariner hath his will.

[1] At once.

112

The Wedding-Guest sat on a stone:
He cannot choose but hear;
And thus spake on that ancient man,
The bright-eyed Mariner.   20

"The ship was cheered, the harbour cleared,
Merrily did we drop
Below the kirk,[2] below the hill,
Below the lighthouse top.

*The Mariner tells how
the ship sailed south-
ward with a good wind
and fair weather, till
it reached the Line.*

The sun came up upon the left,
Out of the sea came he!
And he shone bright, and on the right
Went down into the sea.

Higher and higher every day,
Till over the mast at noon[3]—"   30
The Wedding-Guest here beat his breast,
For he heard the loud bassoon.

*The Wedding-Guest
heareth the bridal
music; but the Mariner
continueth his tale.*

The bride hath paced into the hall,
Red as a rose is she;
Nodding their heads before her goes
The merry minstrelsy.

The Wedding-Guest he beat his breast,
Yet he cannot choose but hear;
And thus spake on that ancient man,
The bright-eyed Mariner.   40

*The ship driven
by a storm toward
the south pole.*

"And now the STORM-BLAST came, and he
Was tyrannous and strong:
He struck with his o'ertaking wings,
And chased us south along.

With sloping masts and dipping prow,
As who pursued with yell and blow

---

2 Church.
3 The ship is at the equator (the "Line").

Still treads the shadow of his foe,
And forward bends his head,
The ship drove fast, loud roared the blast,
And southward aye we fled.   50

And now there came both mist and snow,
And it grew wondrous cold:
And ice, mast-high, came floating by,
As green as emerald.

The land of ice,
and of fearful   And through the drifts the snowy clifts
sounds where no   Did send a dismal sheen:
living thing was to Nor shapes of men nor beasts we ken—
be seen.   The ice was all between.

The ice was here, the ice was there,
The ice was all around: 60
It cracked and growled, and roared and howled,
Like noises in a swound! [4]

Till a great sea-bird,
called the Albatross,   At length did cross an Albatross,
came through the   Thorough the fog it came;
snow-fog, and was   As if it had been a Christian soul,
received with great   We hailed it in God's name.
joy and hospitality.

It ate the food it ne'er had eat,
And round and round it flew.
The ice did split with a thunder-fit;
The helmsman steered us through!   70

And lo! the Albatross
proveth a bird of good   And a good south wind sprung up behind;
omen, and followeth   The Albatross did follow,
the ship as it returned And every day, for food or play,
northward through fog   Came to the mariners' hollo!
and floating ice.

---

[4] Swoon.

In mist or cloud, on mast or shroud,[5]
It perched for vespers nine;
Whiles all the night, through fog-smoke white,
Glimmered the white moon-shine."

The ancient Mariner inhospitably killeth the pious bird of good omen.

"God save thee, ancient Mariner!
From the fiends, that plague thee thus!—   80
Why look'st thou so?"—"With my crossbow
I shot the ALBATROSS."

PART II

"The Sun now rose upon the right:[6]
Out of the sea came he,
Still hid in mist, and on the left
Went down into the sea.

And the good south wind still blew behind,
But no sweet bird did follow,
Nor any day for food or play
Came to the mariners' hollo!   90

His shipmates cry out against the ancient Mariner, for killing the bird of good luck.

And I had done a hellish thing,
And it would work 'em woe:
For all averred, I had killed the bird
That made the breeze to blow.
Ah wretch! said they, the bird to slay,
That made the breeze to blow!

But when the fog cleared off, they justify the same, and thus make themselves accomplices in the crime.

Nor dim nor red, like God's own head,
The glorious Sun uprist:
Then all averred, I had killed the bird
That brought the fog and mist.   100
'Twas right, said they, such birds to slay,
That bring the fog and mist.

---

5 A rope leading from a ship's masthead to support the mast.
6 The ship has rounded Cape Horn and is sailing north into the Pacific.

The fair breeze con-
tinues; the ship
enters the Pacific
Ocean, and sails
northward, even till
it reaches the Line.

The fair breeze blew, the white foam flew,
The furrow followed free;
We were the first that ever burst
Into that silent sea.

The ship hath been
suddenly becalmed.

Down dropt the breeze, the sails dropt down,
'Twas sad as sad could be;
And we did speak only to break
The silence of the sea!   110

All in a hot and copper sky,
The bloody Sun, at noon,
Right up above the mast did stand,
No bigger than the Moon.

Day after day, day after day,
We stuck, nor breath nor motion;
As idle as a painted ship
Upon a painted ocean.

And the Albatross
begins to be avenged.

Water, water, every where,
And all the boards did shrink;   120
Water, water, every where,
Nor any drop to drink.

The very deep did rot: O Christ!
That ever this should be!
Yea, slimy things did crawl with legs
Upon the slimy sea.

About, about, in reel and rout
The death-fires[7] danced at night;
The water, like a witch's oils,
Burnt green, and blue and white.   130

---

[7] St. Elmo's fire, an electric phenomenon often seen in stormy weather on prominent points of a ship and portending disaster.

A Spirit had followed them; one of the invisible inhabitants of this planet, neither departed souls nor angels; concerning whom the learned Jew, Josephus, and the Platonic Constantino-politan, Michael Psellus, may be consulted. They are very numerous, and there is no climate or element without one or more.

And some in dreams assurèd were
Of the Spirit that plagued us so;
Nine fathom deep he had followed us
From the land of mist and snow.

And every tongue, through utter drought,
Was withered at the root;
We could not speak, no more than if
We had been choked with soot.

The ship-mates, in their sore distress, would fain throw the whole guilt on the ancient Mariner: in sign whereof they hang the dead sea-bird round his neck.

Ah! well a-day! what evil looks
Had I from old and young!   140
Instead of the cross, the Albatross
About my neck was hung.

PART III

The ancient Mariner beholdeth a sign in the element afar off.

There passed a weary time. Each throat
Was parched, and glazed each eye.
A weary time! a weary time!
How glazed each weary eye,
When looking westward, I beheld
A something in the sky.

At first it seemed a little speck,
And then it seemed a mist;   150
It moved and moved, and took at last
A certain shape, I wist.[8]

A speck, a mist, a shape, I wist!
And still it neared and neared:
As if it dodged a water-sprite,
It plunged and tacked and veered.

---

[8] Knew.

*At its nearer
approach, it seemeth
him to be a ship; and
at a dear ransom he
freeth his speech from
the bonds of thirst.*

With throats unslaked, with black lips baked,
We could nor laugh nor wail;
Through utter drought all dumb we stood!
I bit my arm, I sucked the blood,   160
And cried, A sail! a sail!

A flash of joy;

With throats unslaked, with black lips baked,
Agape they heard me call:
Gramercy![9] they for joy did grin,
And all at once their breath drew in,
As they were drinking all.

*And horror follows.
For can it be a ship
that comes onward
without wind or tide?*

See! see! (I cried) she tacks no more!
Hither to work us weal;[10]
Without a breeze, without a tide,
She steadies with upright keel!   170

The western wave was all aflame,
The day was well nigh done!
Almost upon the western wave
Rested the broad bright Sun;
When that strange shape drove suddenly
Betwixt us and the Sun.

*It seemeth him but
the skeleton of a ship.*

And straight the Sun was flecked with bars,
(Heaven's Mother send us grace!)
As if through a dungeon-grate he peered
With broad and burning face.   180

Alas! (thought I, and my heart beat loud)
How fast she nears and nears!
Are those her sails that glance in the Sun,
Like restless gossameres?

---

[9] Great thanks.
[10] Benefit.

And its ribs are seen as bars on the face of the setting Sun. The Spectre-Woman and her Death-mate, and no other on board the skeleton ship.

Are those her ribs through which the Sun
Did peer, as through a grate?
And is that Woman all her crew?
Is that a DEATH? and are there two?
Is DEATH that woman's mate?

Like vessel, like crew!

Her lips were red, her looks were free,   190
Her locks were yellow as gold:
Her skin was as white as leprosy,
The Nightmare LIFE-IN-DEATH was she,
Who thicks man's blood with cold.

Death and Life-in-Death have diced for the ship's crew, and she (the latter) winneth the ancient Mariner.

The naked hulk alongside came,
And the twain were casting dice;
'The game is done! I've won! I've won!'
Quoth she, and whistles thrice.

No twilight within the courts of the Sun.

The Sun's rim dips; the stars rush out:
At one stride comes the dark;   200
With far-heard whisper, o'er the sea,
Off shot the spectre-bark.

At the rising of the Moon,

We listened and looked sideways up!
Fear at my heart, as at a cup,
My life-blood seemed to sip!
The stars were dim, and thick the night,
The steersman's face by his lamp gleamed white;
From the sails the dew did drip—
Till clomb above the eastern bar
The hornèd Moon, with one bright star   210
Within the nether tip.

One after another,

One after one, by the star-dogged Moon,
Too quick for groan or sigh,
Each turned his face with a ghastly pang,
And cursed me with his eye.

His ship-mates drop
down dead.

Four times fifty living men
(And I heard nor sigh nor groan)
With heavy thump, a lifeless lump,
They dropped down one by one.

But Life-in-Death
begins her work on
the ancient Mariner.

The souls did from their bodies fly—   220
They fled to bliss or woe!
And every soul, it passed me by,
Like the whizz of my cross-bow!"

PART IV

The Wedding-Guest
feareth that a Spirit
is talking to him;

"I fear thee, ancient Mariner!
I fear thy skinny hand!
And thou art long, and lank, and brown,
As is the ribbed sea-sand.

"I fear thee and thy glittering eye,
And thy skinny hand, so brown."—
But the ancient
Mariner assureth
him of his bodily
life, and proceedeth
to relate his horrible
penance.
"Fear not, fear not, thou Wedding-Guest!   230
This body dropt not down.

Alone, alone, all, all alone,
Alone on a wide wide sea!
And never a saint took pity on
My soul in agony.

He despiseth the
creatures of the calm.

The many men, so beautiful!
And they all dead did lie:
And a thousand thousand slimy things
Lived on; and so did I.

And envieth that
they should live, and
so many lie dead.

I looked upon the rotting sea,   240
And drew my eyes away;
I looked upon the rotting deck,
And there the dead men lay.

I looked to heaven, and tried to pray;
But or ever a prayer had gusht,
A wicked whisper came, and made
My heart as dry as dust.

I closed my lids, and kept them close,
And the balls like pulses beat;
For the sky and the sea, and the sea and
    the sky,   250
Lay like a load on my weary eye,
And the dead were at my feet.

But the curse liveth
for him in the eye
of the dead men.

The cold sweat melted from their limbs,
Nor rot nor reek did they:
The look with which they looked on me
Had never passed away.

An orphan's curse would drag to hell
A spirit from on high;
But oh! more horrible than that
Is the curse in a dead man's eye!   260
Seven days, seven nights, I saw that curse,
And yet I could not die.

In his loneliness and
fixedness he yearneth
towards the journeying
Moon, and the stars
that still sojourn, yet
still move onward; and
every where the blue
sky belongs to them,
and is their appointed
rest, and their native
country and their own
natural homes,
which they enter
unannounced, as lords
that are certainly
expected and yet there
is a silent joy at
their arrival.

The moving Moon went up the sky,
And nowhere did abide:
Softly she was going up,
And a star or two beside—

Her beams bemocked the sultry main,
Like April hoar-frost spread;
But where the ship's huge shadow lay,
The charmèd water burnt alway   270
A still and awful red.

*By the light of the
Moon he beholdeth
God's creatures of the
great calm.*

Beyond the shadow of the ship,
I watched the water-snakes:
They moved in tracks of shining white,
And when they reared, the elfish light
Fell off in hoary flakes.

Within the shadow of the ship
I watched their rich attire:
Blue, glossy green, and velvet black,
They coiled and swam; and every track   280
Was a flash of golden fire.

*Their beauty and their
happiness.*

*He blesseth them in
his heart.*

O happy living things! no tongue
Their beauty might declare:
A spring of love gushed from my heart,
And I blessed them unaware:
Sure my kind saint took pity on me,
And I blessed them unaware.

*The spell begins to
break.*

The selfsame moment I could pray;
And from my neck so free
The Albatross fell off, and sank   290
Like lead into the sea.

PART V

"Oh, sleep! it is a gentle thing,
Beloved from pole to pole!
To Mary Queen the praise be given!
She sent the gentle sleep from Heaven,
That slid into my soul.

*By grace of the holy
Mother, the ancient
Mariner is refreshed
with rain.*

The silly[11] buckets on the deck,
That had so long remained,
I dreamt that they were filled with dew;
And when I awoke, it rained.   300

My lips were wet, my throat was cold,
My garments all were dank;

---

[11] Useless, hence empty.

Sure I had drunken in my dreams,
And still my body drank.

I moved, and could not feel my limbs:
I was so light—almost
I thought that I had died in sleep,
And was a blessèd ghost.

*He heareth sounds
and seeth strange
sights and commotions
in the sky and
the element.*

And soon I heard a roaring wind:
It did not come anear;   310
But with its sound it shook the sails,
That were so thin and sere.

The upper air burst into life!
And a hundred fire-flags sheen,[12]
To and fro they were hurried about!
And to and fro, and in and out,
The wan stars danced between.

And the coming wind did roar more loud,
And the sails did sigh like sedge;[13]
And the rain poured down from one
          black cloud;   320
The Moon was at its edge.

The thick black cloud was cleft, and still
The Moon was at its side:
Like waters shot from some high crag,
The lightning fell with never a jag,
A river steep and wide.

*The bodies of the
ship's crew are in-
spired, and the ship
moves on;*

The loud wind never reached the ship,
Yet now the ship moved on!
Beneath the lightning and the Moon
The dead men gave a groan.   330

They groaned, they stirred, they all uprose,
Nor spake, nor moved their eyes;

---

12 Aurora Australis, Southern Lights.
13 Marsh plant.

It had been strange, even in a dream,
To have seen those dead men rise.

The helmsman steered, the ship moved on;
Yet never a breeze up-blew;
The mariners all 'gan work the ropes,
Where they were wont to do;
They raised their limbs like lifeless tools—
We were a ghastly crew.   340

The body of my brother's son
Stood by me, knee to knee:
The body and I pulled at one rope,
But he said nought to me."

"I fear thee, ancient Mariner!"
"Be calm, thou Wedding-Guest!

*But not by the souls
of the men, nor by
demons of earth or
middle air, but by
a blessed troop of
angelic spirits, sent
down by the invoca-
tion of the guardian
saint.*

'Twas not those souls that fled in pain,
Which to their corses came again,
But a troop of spirits blest:

For when it dawned—they dropped
          their arms,   350
And clustered round the mast;
Sweet sounds rose slowly through their mouths,
And from their bodies passed.

Around, around, flew each sweet sound,
Then darted to the Sun;
Slowly the sounds came back again,
Now mixed, now one by one.

Sometimes a-dropping from the sky
I heard the sky-lark sing;
Sometimes all little birds that are,   360
How they seemed to fill the sea and air
With their sweet jargoning![14]

---

[14] Warbling.

And now 'twas like all instruments,
Now like a lonely flute;
And now it is an angel's song,
That makes the heavens be mute.

It ceased; yet still the sails made on
A pleasant noise till noon,
A noise like of a hidden brook
In the leafy month of June,   370
That to the sleeping woods all night
Singeth a quiet tune.

Till noon we quietly sailed on,
Yet never a breeze did breathe:
Slowly and smoothly went the ship,
Moved onward from beneath.

The lonesome Spirit
from the south-pole
carries on the ship as
far as the Line, in
obedience to the
angelic troop, but
still requireth
vengeance.

Under the keel nine fathom deep,
From the land of mist and snow,
The spirit slid: and it was he
That made the ship to go.   380
The sails at noon left off their tune,
And the ship stood still also.

The Sun, right up above the mast,
Had fixed her to the ocean:
But in a minute she 'gan stir,
With a short uneasy motion—
Backwards and forwards half her length,
With a short uneasy motion.

Then like a pawing horse let go,
She made a sudden bound: 390
It flung the blood into my head,
And I fell down in a swound.

The Polar Spirit's
fellow-daemons, the
invisible inhabitants
of the element, take
part in his wrong;
and two of them relate,
one to the other, that
penance long and heavy
for the ancient Mariner
hath been accorded to
the Polar Spirit, who
returneth southward.

How long in that same fit I lay,
I have not[15] to declare;
But ere my living life returned,
I heard, and in my soul discerned
Two voices in the air.

'Is it he?' quoth one, 'Is this the man?
By him who died on cross,
With his cruel bow he laid full low   400
The harmless Albatross.

The spirit who bideth by himself
In the land of mist and snow,
He loved the bird that loved the man
Who shot him with his bow.'

The other was a softer voice,
As soft as honey-dew:
Quoth he, "The man hath penance done,
And penance more will do.'

PART VI

First Voice

'But tell me, tell me! speak again   410
Thy soft response renewing—
What makes that ship drive on so fast?
What is the ocean doing?'

Second Voice

'Still as a slave before his lord,
The ocean hath no blast;
His great bright eye most silently
Up to the Moon is cast—

If he may know which way to go;
For she guides him smooth or grim.

---

[15] I have not the knowledge to declare.

See, brother, see! how graciously   420
She looketh down on him.'

First Voice

'But why drives on that ship so fast,
Without or wave or wind?'

Second Voice

'The air is cut away before,
And closes from behind.

Fly, brother, fly! more high, more high!
Or we shall be belated:
For slow and slow that ship will go,
When the Mariner's trance is abated.'

The Mariner hath been cast into a trance; for the angelic power causeth the vessel to drive northward faster than human life could endure.

I woke, and we were sailing on   430
As in a gentle weather:
'Twas night, calm night, the moon was high;
The dead men stood together.

The supernatural motion is retarded; the Mariner awakes, and his penance begins anew.

All stood together on the deck,
For a charnel-dungeon fitter:
All fixed on me their stony eyes,
That in the Moon did glitter.

The pang, the curse, with which they died,
Had never passed away:
I could not draw my eyes from theirs,   440
Nor turn them up to pray.

The curse is finally expiated.

And now this spell was snapt: once more
I viewed the ocean green,
And looked far forth, yet little saw
Of what had else been seen—

Like one, that on a lonesome road
Doth walk in fear and dread,

And having once turned round walks on,
And turns no more his head;
Because he knows, a frightful fiend   450
Doth close behind him tread.

But soon there breathed a wind on me,
Nor sound nor motion made:
Its path was not upon the sea,
In ripple or in shade.

It raised my hair, it fanned my cheek
Like a meadow-gale of spring—
It mingled strangely with my fears,
Yet it felt like a welcoming.

Swiftly, swiftly flew the ship,   460
Yet she sailed softly too:
Sweetly, sweetly blew the breeze—
On me alone it blew.

And the ancient
Mariner beholdeth
his native country.

Oh! dream of joy! is this indeed
The light-house top I see?
Is this the hill? is this the kirk?
Is this mine own countree?

We drifted o'er the harbour-bar,
And I with sobs did pray—
O let me be awake, my God!   470
Or let me sleep alway.

The harbour-bay was clear as glass,
So smoothly it was strewn!
And on the bay the moonlight lay,
And the shadow of the Moon.

The rock shone bright, the kirk no less,
That stands above the rock:
The moonlight steeped in silentness
The steady weathercock.

And the bay was white with silent light,   480
Till rising from the same,
The angelic spirits leave the dead bodies, Full many shapes, that shadows were,
In crimson colors came.

And appear in their own forms of light. A little distance from the prow
Those crimson shadows were:
I turned my eyes upon the deck—
Oh, Christ! what saw I there!

Each corse lay flat, lifeless and flat,
And, by the holy rood![16]
A man all light, a seraph-man,[17]   490
On every corse there stood.

This seraph-band, each waved his hand:
It was a heavenly sight!
They stood as signals to the land,
Each one a lovely light;

This seraph-band, each waved his hand,
No voice did they impart—
No voice; but oh! the silence sank
Like music on my heart.

But soon I heard the dash of oars,   500
I heard the Pilot's cheer;
My head was turned perforce away,
And I saw a boat appear.

The Pilot and the Pilot's boy,
I heard them coming fast:
Dear Lord in Heaven! it was a joy
The dead men could not blast.

---

[16] Cross.
[17] A seraph is the highest rank of the angels.

I saw a third—I heard his voice:
It is the Hermit good!
He singeth loud his godly hymns   510
That he makes in the wood.
He'll shrieve my soul, he'll wash away
The Albatross's blood.

PART VII

*The Hermit of
the Wood,*

This Hermit good lives in that wood
Which slopes down to the sea.
How loudly his sweet voice he rears!
He loves to talk with marineres
That come from a far countree.

He kneels at morn, and noon, and eve—
He hath a cushion plump: 520
It is the moss that wholly hides
The rotted old oak-stump.

The skiff-boat neared: I heard them talk,
'Why, this is strange, I trow!
Where are those lights so many and fair,
That signal made but now?'

*Approacheth the
ship with wonder.*

'Strange, by my faith!' the Hermit said—
'And they answered not our cheer!
The planks looked warped! and see those sails,
How thin they are and sere!   530
I never saw aught like to them,
Unless perchance it were

Brown skeletons of leaves that lag
My forest-brook along;
When the ivy-tod[18] is heavy with snow,
And the owlet whoops to the wolf below,
That eats the she-wolf's young.'

---

[18] Ivy bush.

'Dear Lord! it hath a fiendish look—
(The Pilot made reply)
I am a-feared'—'Push on, push on!'   540
Said the Hermit cheerily.

The boat came closer to the ship,
But I nor spake nor stirred;
The boat came close beneath the ship,
And straight a sound was heard.

The ship suddenly   Under the water it rumbled on,
sinketh.   Still louder and more dread:
                              It reached the ship, it split the bay;
                              The ship went down like lead.

The ancient Mariner   Stunned by that loud and dreadful sound,   550
is saved in the   Which sky and ocean smote,
Pilot's boat.   Like one that hath been seven days drowned,
                              My body lay afloat;
                              But swift as dreams, myself I found
                              Within the Pilot's boat.

Upon the whirl, where sank the ship,
The boat spun round and round;
And all was still, save that the hill
Was telling of the sound.

I moved my lips—the Pilot shrieked,   560
And fell down in a fit;
The holy Hermit raised his eyes,
And prayed where he did sit.

I took the oars: the Pilot's boy,
Who now doth crazy go,
Laughed loud and long, and all the while
His eyes went to and fro.
'Ha! ha!' quoth he, 'full plain I see,
The Devil knows how to row.'

And now, all in my own countree,   570
I stood on the firm land!
The Hermit stepped forth from the boat,
And scarcely he could stand.

The ancient Mariner
earnestly entreateth
the Hermit to shrieve
him; and the penance
of life falls on him.

'O shrieve me, shrieve me, holy man!'
The Hermit crossed his brow,[19]
'Say quick,' quoth he, 'I bid thee say—
What manner of man art thou?'

Forthwith this frame of mine was wrenched
With a woeful agony,
Which forced me to begin my tale;   580
And then it left me free.

And ever and anon
throughout his future
life an agony con-
straineth him to travel
from land to land;

Since then, at an uncertain hour,
That agony returns;
And till my ghastly tale is told,
This heart within me burns.

I pass, like night, from land to land;
I have strange power of speech;
That moment that his face I see,
I know the man that must hear me:
To him my tale I teach.   590

What loud uproar bursts from that door!
The wedding-guests are there;
But in the garden-bower the bride
And bride-maids singing are:
And hark the little vesper bell,
Which biddeth me to prayer!

O Wedding-Guest! this soul hath been
Alone on a wide wide sea:
So lonely 'twas, that God himself
Scarce seemèd there to be.   600

---

[19] Made the sign of the cross on his forehead.

O sweeter than the marriage-feast.
'Tis sweeter far to me,
To walk together to the kirk
With a goodly company!—

To walk together to the kirk,
And all together pray,
While each to his great Father bends,
Old men, and babes, and loving friends
And youths and maidens gay!

And to teach, by his own example, love and reverence to all things that God made and loveth.

Farewell, farewell! but this I tell   610
To thee, thou Wedding-Guest!
He prayeth well, who loveth well
Both man and bird and beast.

He prayeth best, who loveth best
All things both great and small;
For the dear God who loveth us,
He made and loveth all."

The Mariner, whose eye is bright,
Whose beard with age is hoar,
Is gone: and now the Wedding-Guest   620
Turned from the bridegroom's door.

He went like one that hath been stunned,
And is of sense forlorn:[20]
A sadder and a wiser man,
He rose the morrow morn.

---

[20] Deprived of his senses.

Questions for Discussion

1. Compare Lear's actions in *King Lear* and those of the Ancient Mariner, particularly the arbitrary dismissal of Cordelia and the arbitrary killing of the Albatross, the subsequent suffering and isolation of the hero and his repentance for his act.

2. Why is the ballad form appropriate for the story?

3. Why is the Wedding Guest an apt listener for the Ancient Mariner's tale? Give the reason he interrupts the Ancient Mariner each time. Is there any change in his attitude as the poem progresses?

4. Outline the stages in the Mariner's suffering and repentance, noting the supernatural aspects of it.

5. What is the significance of the sinking of the ship in Part VII?

6. What specifically is the Ancient Mariner's crime?

7. Coleridge wrote: "The romance-writer possesses an unlimited power over situations, but he must scrupulously make his characters act in congruity with them." Explain how he does this in the poem.

8. How do you know that Coleridge is more interested in the human truths the supernatural events portray than the events themselves?

9. Note the contrast between the natural (the Kirk, the Wedding Guest, and the Hermit) and the supernatural (the Death Ship, the Spirits, and the Mariner's Crew). How is such a contrast appropriate for a romance? What effect does it achieve?

John Keats (1795–1821)

La Belle Dame Sans Merci[1]

O what can ail thee, Knight at arms,
  Alone and palely loitering?
The sedge has withered from the Lake
  And no birds sing!

O what can ail thee, Knight at arms,
  So haggard, and so woebegone?
The squirrel's granary is full
  And the harvest's done.

I see a lily on thy brow
  With anguish moist and fever dew,   10
And on thy cheeks a fading rose
  Fast withereth too.

I met a Lady in the Meads,[2]
  Full beautiful, a faery's child,
Her hair was long, her foot was light
  And her eyes were wild.

I made a Garland for her head,
  And bracelets too, and fragrant Zone;[3]
She looked at me as she did love
  And made sweet moan.   20

I set her on my pacing steed
  And nothing else saw all day long,

---

[1] The beautiful lady without pity.
[2] The knight begins to speak here.
[3] Girdle.

135

For sidelong would she bend and sing
   A faery's song.

She found me roots of relish sweet,
   And honey wild, and manna dew,
And sure in language strange she said
   "I love thee true."

She took me to her elfin grot
   And there she wept and sighed full sore,   30
And there I shut her wild wild eyes
   With kisses four.

And there she lulléd me asleep,
   And there I dreamed, Ah Woe betide!
The latest[4] dream I ever dreamt
   On the cold hill side.

I saw pale Kings, and Princes too,
   Pale warriors, death-pale were they all;
They cried, "La belle dame sans merci
   Thee hath in thrall[5]!"   40

I saw their starved lips in the gloam
   With horrid warning gapéd wide,
And I awoke, and found me here
   On the cold hill's side.

And this is why I sojourn here,
   Alone and palely loitering;
Though the sedge is withered from the Lake
   And no birds sing.

---

[4] Last.
[5] Bondage.

Questions for Discussion

1. How does "La Belle Dame Sans Merci" differ from a folk ballad? Consider specifically the language, the verse form, and the development of the situation.

2. What word is the most important one in the description of the fairy child? What is its significance?

3. What is the significance of the dream and the ghoulish characters the Knight envisages?

4. Contrast the attitudes about the autumnal setting stated by the first speaker and the knight.

5. Explain the symbolism of the lily and the rose in the third stanza.

Alfred, Lord Tennyson (1809–1892)

The Lady of Shalott

PART 1

On either side the river lie
Long fields of barley and of rye,
That clothe the wold[1] and meet the sky;
And through the field the road runs by
    To many-towered Camelot;[2]
And up and down the people go,
Gazing where the lilies blow[3]
Round an island there below,
    The island of Shalott.

Willows whiten, aspens quiver,   10
Little breezes dusk and shiver
Through the wave that runs forever
By the island in the river
    Flowing down to Camelot.
Four gray walls, and four gray towers,
Overlook a space of flowers,
And the silent isle embowers
    The Lady of Shalott.

By the margin, willow-veiled,
Slide the heavy barges trailed   20
By slow horses; and unhailed
The shallop[4] flitteth silken-sailed
    Skimming down to Camelot:

---

[1] A plain.
[2] City in which King Arthur's court was supposed to be located.
[3] Bloom.
[4] A light, open boat.

But who hath seen her wave her hand?
Or at the casement seen her stand?
Or is she known in all the land,
    The Lady of Shalott?

Only reapers, reaping early
In among the bearded barley,
Hear a song that echoes cheerly   30
From the river winding clearly,
    Down to towered Camelot;
And by the moon the reaper weary,
Piling sheaves in uplands airy,
Listening, whispers, " 'Tis the fairy
    Lady of Shalott."

PART 2

There she weaves by night and day
A magic web with colors gay.
She has heard a whisper say,
A curse is on her if she stay   40
    To look down to Camelot.
She knows not what the curse may be,
And so she weaveth steadily,
And little other care hath she,
    The Lady of Shalott.

And moving through a mirror clear
That hangs before her all the year,
Shadows of the world appear.
There she sees the highway near
    Winding down to Camelot;   50
There the river eddy whirls,
And there the surly village-churls,
And the red cloaks of market girls,
    Pass onward from Shalott.

Sometimes a troop of damsels glad,
An abbot on an ambling pad,[5]

---

[5] A horse that moves along at an easy pace.

Sometimes a curly shepherd-lad,
Or long-haired page in crimson clad,
    Goes by to towered Camelot;
And sometimes through the mirror blue   60
The knights come riding two and two;
She hath no loyal knight and true,
    The Lady of Shalott.

But in her web she still delights
To weave the mirror's magic sights,
For often through the silent nights
A funeral, with plumes and lights
    And music, went to Camelot;
Or when the moon was overhead,
Came two young lovers lately wed;   70
"I am half sick of shadows," said
    The Lady of Shalott.

PART 3

A bow-shot from her bower eaves,
He rode between the barley sheaves;
The sun came dazzling through the leaves,
And flamed upon the brazen greaves[6]
    Of bold Sir Lancelot.
A red-cross knight forever kneeled
To a lady in his shield,
That sparkled on the yellow field,   80
    Beside remote Shalott.

The gemmy bridle glittered free,
Like to some branch of stars we see
Hung in the golden Galaxy.
The bridle bells rang merrily
    As he rode down to Camelot;
And from his blazoned baldric[7] slung
A mighty silver bugle hung,
And as he rode his armor rung,
    Beside remote Shalott.   90

---

[6] Armor for the leg below the knee.
[7] A belt worn over the shoulder to support a sword or bugle.

All in the blue unclouded weather
Thick-jeweled shone the saddle-leather,
The helmet and the helmet-feather
Burned like one burning flame together
 As he rode down to Camelot;
As often through the purple night,
Below the starry clusters bright,
Some bearded meteor, trailing light,
 Moves over still Shalott.

His broad clear brow in sunlight glowed;   100
On burnished hooves his war horse trode;
From underneath his helmet flowed
His coal-black curls as on he rode,
 As he rode down to Camelot.
From the band and from the river
He flashed into the crystal mirror,
"Tirra lirra," by the river
 Sang Sir Lancelot.

She left the web, she left the loom,
She made three paces through the room,   110
She saw the water lily bloom,
She saw the helmet and the plume,
 She looked down to Camelot.
Out flew the web and floated wide;
The mirror cracked from side to side;
"The curse is come upon me," cried
 The Lady of Shalott.

PART 4

In the stormy east wind straining,
The pale yellow woods were waning,
The broad stream in his banks complaining, 120
Heavily the low sky raining
 Over towered Camelot;
Down she came and found a boat
Beneath a willow left afloat,
And round about the prow she wrote
 THE LADY OF SHALOTT.

And down the river's dim expanse
Like some bold seër in a trance,
Seeing all his own mischance—
With a glassy countenance   130
    Did she look to Camelot.
And at the closing of the day
She loosed the chain, and down she lay;
The broad stream bore her far away,
    The Lady of Shalott.

Lying, robed in snowy white
That loosely flew to left and right—
The leaves upon her falling light—
Through the noises of the night
    She floated down to Camelot;   140
And as the boat-head wound along
The willowy hills and fields among,
They heard her singing her last song,
    The Lady of Shalott.

Heard a carol, mournful, holy,
Chanted loudly, chanted lowly,
Till her blood was frozen slowly,
And her eyes were darkened wholly,
    Turned to towered Camelot.
For ere she reached upon the tide   150
The first house by the waterside,
Singing in her song she died,
    The Lady of Shalott.

Under tower and balcony,
By garden wall and gallery,
A gleaming shape she floated by,
Dead-pale between the houses high,
    Silent into Camelot.
Out upon the wharfs they came,
Knight and burgher, lord and dame,   160
And round the prow they read her name,
    THE LADY OF SHALOTT.

Who is this? and what is here?
And in the lighted palace near
Died the sound of royal cheer;
And they crossed themselves for fear,
    All the knights at Camelot:
But Lancelot mused a little space;
He said, "She has a lovely face;
God in his mercy lend her grace,   170
    The Lady of Shalott."

Questions for Discussion

1. How is "The Lady of Shalott" related to the ballad in technique as well as subject matter?

2. What does the poem have in common with medieval romance?

3. Tennyson said of the heroine at the end of Part 2: "The new-born love for something, for someone in the wide world from which she has been so long excluded, takes her out of the region of shadows into that of realities." Relate this quotation to the poem. Is this true of other heroines of romance?

4. Is there any significance in the fact that the language and imagery of Part 3 are much more vivid than in any other part of the poem?

5. Explain the symbolism of the mirror and the meaning of its cracking at the end of Part 3.

Alexander Pushkin (1799–1837)

The Queen of Spades

TRANSLATED BY T. KEANE

There was a card party at the rooms of Narumov of the Horse Guards. The long winter night passed away imperceptibly, and it was five o'clock in the morning before the company sat down to supper. Those who had won, ate with a good appetite; the others sat staring absently at their empty plates. When the champagne appeared, however, the conversation became more animated, and all took a part in it.

"And how did you fare, Surin?" asked the host.

"Oh, I lost, as usual. I must confess that I am unlucky: I play mirandole, I always keep cool, I never allow anything to put me out, and yet I always lose!"

"And you did not once allow yourself to be tempted to back the red? . . . Your firmness astonishes me."

"But what do you think of Hermann?" said one of the guests, pointing to a young Engineer. "He has never had a card in his hand in his life, he has never in his life laid a wager, and yet he sits here till five o'clock in the morning watching our play."

"Play interests me very much," said Hermann, "but I am not in the position to sacrifice the necessary in the hope of winning the superfluous."

"Hermann is a German: he is economical—that is all!" observed Tomsky. "But if there is one person that I cannot understand, it is my grandmother, the Countess Anna Fedotovna."

"How so?" inquired the guests.

"I cannot understand," continued Tomsky, "how it is that my grandmother does not play."

"The Queen of Spades" by Alexander Pushkin, from *Pushkin's Prose Tales* translated by T. Keane. Reprinted by permission of G. Bell & Sons, Ltd.

"What is there remarkable about an old lady of eighty not playing?" said Narumov.

"Then you do not know the reason why?"

"No, really; haven't the faintest idea."

"Oh! then listen. About sixty years ago, my grandmother went to Paris, where she created quite a sensation. People used to run after her to catch a glimpse of the 'Muscovite Venus.' Richelieu made love to her, and my grandmother maintains that he almost blew out his brains in consequence of her cruelty. At that time ladies used to play at faro. On one occasion at the Court, she lost a very considerable sum to the Duke of Orleans. On returning home, my grandmother removed the patches from her face, took off her hoops, informed my grandfather of her loss at the gaming-table, and ordered him to pay the money. My deceased grandfather, as far as I remember, was a sort of house-steward to my grandmother. He dreaded her like fire; but, on hearing of such a heavy loss, he almost went out of his mind; he calculated the various sums she had lost, and pointed out to her that in six months she had spent half a million francs, that neither their Moscow nor Saratov estates were in Paris, and finally refused point blank to pay the debt. My grandmother gave him a box on the ear and slept by herself as a sign of her displeasure. The next day she sent for her husband, hoping that this domestic punishment had produced an effect upon him, but she found him inflexible. For the first time in her life, she entered into reasonings and explanations with him, thinking to be able to convince him by pointing out to him that there are debts and debts, and that there is a great difference between a Prince and a coachmaker. But it was all in vain, my grandfather still remained obdurate. But the matter did not rest there. My grandmother did not know what to do. She had shortly before become acquainted with a very remarkable man. You have heard of Count St. Germain, about whom so many marvellous stories are told. You know that he represented himself as the Wandering Jew, as the discoverer of the elixir of life, of the philosopher's stone, and so forth. Some laughed at him as a charlatan; but Casanova, in his memoirs, says that he was a spy. But be that as it may, St. Germain, in spite of the mystery surrounding him, was a very fascinating person, and was much sought after in the best circles of society. Even to this day my grandmother retains an affectionate recollection of him, and becomes quite angry if any one speaks disrespectfully of him. My grandmother knew that St. Germain had large sums of money at his disposal. She resolved to have recourse to him, and she wrote a letter to him asking him to come to her without delay. The queer old man immediately waited upon her and found her overwhelmed with grief. She described to him in the blackest colours the barbarity of her husband, and ended by declaring that her whole hope depended upon his friendship and amiability.

"St. Germain reflected.

" 'I could advance you the sum you want,' said he; 'but I know that you would not rest easy until you had paid me back, and I should not like to bring fresh troubles upon you. But there is another way of getting out of your difficulty: you can win back your money.'

" 'But, my dear Count,' replied my grandmother, 'I tell you that I haven't any money left.'

" 'Money is not necessary,' replied St. Germain. 'Be pleased to listen to me.'

"Then he revealed to her a secret, for which each of us would give a good deal . . ."

The young officers listened with increased attention. Tomsky lit his pipe, puffed away for a moment and then continued:

"That same evening my grandmother went to Versailles to the *jeu de la reine*. The Duke of Orleans kept the bank; my grandmother excused herself in an off-hand manner for not having yet paid her debt, by inventing some little story, and then began to play against him. She chose three cards and played them one after the other: all three won *sonika*,[1] and my grandmother recovered every farthing that she had lost."

"Mere chance!" said one of the guests.

"A tale!" observed Hermann.

"Perhaps they were marked cards!" said a third.

"I do not think so," replied Tomsky gravely.

"What!" said Narumov, "you have a grandmother who knows how to hit upon three lucky cards in succession, and you have never yet succeeded in getting the secret of it out of her?"

"That's the deuce of it!" replied Tomsky. "She had four sons, one of whom was my father; all four were determined gamblers, and yet not to one of them did she ever reveal her secret, although it would not have been a bad thing either for them or for me. But this is what I heard from my uncle, Count Ivan Ilyich, and he assured me, on his honour, that it was true. The late Chaplitzky—the same who died in poverty after having squandered millions—once lost, in his youth, about three hundred thousand rubles—to Zorich, if I remember rightly. He was in despair. My grandmother, who was always very severe upon the extravagance of young men, took pity, however, upon Chaplitzky. She gave him three cards, telling him to play them one after the other, at the same time exacting from him a solemn promise that he would never play at cards again as long as he lived. Chaplitzky then went to his victorious opponent, and they began a fresh game. On the first card he staked fifty thousand rubles and won *sonika*; he doubled the stake and

---

[1] Said of a card when it wins or loses in the quickest possible time.

won again, till at last, by pursuing the same tactics, he won back more than
he had lost . . .

"But it is time to go to bed: it is a quarter to six already."

And indeed it was already beginning to dawn: the young men emptied
their glasses and then took leave of each other.

II

The old Countess A—— was seated in her dressing-room in front of her
looking-glass. Three waiting maids stood around her. One held a small pot
of rouge, another a box of hair-pins, and the third a tall cap with bright red
ribbons. The Countess had no longer the slightest pretensions to beauty, but
she still preserved the habits of her youth, dressed in strict accordance with
the fashion of seventy years before, and made as long and as careful a toilette
as she would have done sixty years previously. Near the window, at an
embroidery frame, sat a young lady, her ward.

"Good morning, grandmamma," said a young officer, entering the room.
"*Bonjour, Mademoiselle Lise.* Grandmamma, I want to ask you something."

"What is it, Paul?"

"I want you to let me introduce one of my friends to you, and to allow
me to bring him to the ball on Friday."

"Bring him direct to the ball and introduce him to me there. Were you
at B——'s yesterday?"

"Yes; everything went off very pleasantly, and dancing was kept up until
five o'clock. How charming Yeletzkaya was!"

"But, my dear, what is there charming about her? Isn't she like her
grandmother, the Princess Daria Petrovna? By the way, she must be very
old, the Princess Daria Petrovna."

"How do you mean, old?" cried Tomsky thoughtlessly; "she died seven
years ago."

The young lady raised her head and made a sign to the young officer. He
then remembered that the old Countess was never to be informed of the
death of any of her contemporaries, and he bit his lips. But the old Countess
heard the news with the greatest indifference.

"Dead!" said she; "and I did not know it. We were appointed maids of
honour at the same time, and when we were presented to the Empress. . . ."

And the Countess for the hundredth time related to her grandson one of
her anecdotes.

"Come, Paul," said she, when she had finished her story, "help me to
get up. Lizanka, where is my snuff-box?"

And the Countess with her three maids went behind a screen to finish her
toilette. Tomsky was left alone with the young lady.

"Who is the gentleman you wish to introduce to the Countess?" asked Lizaveta Ivanovna in a whisper.

"Narumov. Do you know him?"

"No. Is he a soldier or a civilian?"

"A soldier."

"Is he in the Engineers?"

"No, in the Cavalry. What made you think he was in the Engineers?"

The young lady smiled, but made no reply.

"Paul," cried the Countess from behind the screen, "send me some new novel, only pray don't let it be one of the present day style."

"What do you mean, grandmother?"

"That is, a novel, in which the hero strangles neither his father nor his mother, and in which there are no drowned bodies. I have a great horror of drowned persons."

"There are no such novels nowadays. Would you like a Russian one?"

"Are there any Russian novels? Send me one, my dear, pray send me one!"

"Good-bye, grandmother; I am in a hurry. . . . Good-bye, Lizaveta Ivanovna. What made you think that Narumov was in the Engineers?"

And Tomsky left the boudoir.

Lizaveta Ivanovna was left alone: she laid aside her work and began to look out of the window. A few moments afterwards, at a corner house on the other side of the street, a young officer appeared. A deep blush covered her cheeks; she took up her work again and bent her head down over the frame. At the same moment the Countess returned completely dressed.

"Order the carriage, Lizaveta," said she; "we will go out for a drive."

Lizaveta arose from the frame and began to arrange her work.

"What is the matter with you, my child, are you deaf?" cried the Countess. "Order the carriage to be got ready at once."

"I will do so this moment," replied the young lady, hastening into the ante-room.

A servant entered and gave the Countess some books from Prince Paul Aleksandrovich.

"Tell him that I am obliged to him," said the Countess. "Lizaveta! Lizaveta! where are you running to?"

"I am going to dress."

"There is plenty of time, my dear. Sit down here. Open the first volume and read to me aloud."

Her companion took the book and read a few lines.

"Louder," said the Countess. "What is the matter with you, my child? Have you lost your voice? Wait—give me that footstool—a little nearer—that will do."

Lizaveta read two more pages. The Countess yawned.

"Put the book down," said she. "What a lot of nonsense! Send it back to Prince Paul with my thanks. . . . But where is the carriage?"

"The carriage is ready," said Lizaveta, looking out into the street.

"How is it that you are not dressed?" said the Countess. "I must always wait for you. It is intolerable, my dear!"

Liza hastened to her room. She had not been there two minutes, before the Countess began to ring with all her might. The three waiting-maids came running in at one door and the valet at another.

"How is it that you cannot hear me when I ring for you?" said the Countess. "Tell Lizaveta Ivanovna that I am waiting for her."

Lizaveta returned with her hat and cloak on.

"At last you are here!" said the Countess. "But why such an elaborate toilette? Whom do you intend to captivate? What sort of weather is it? It seems rather windy."

"No, your Ladyship, it is very calm," replied the valet.

"You never think of what you are talking about. Open the window. So it is: windy and bitterly cold. Unharness the horses. Lizaveta, we won't go out— there was no need for you to deck yourself like that."

"What a life is mine!" thought Lizaveta Ivanovna.

And, in truth, Lizaveta Ivanovna was a very unfortunate creature. "The bread of the stranger is bitter," says Dante, "and his staircase hard to climb." But who can know what the bitterness of dependence is so well as the poor companion of an old lady of quality? The Countess A—— had by no means a bad heart, but she was capricious, like a woman who had been spoilt by the world, as well as being avaricious and egotistical, like all old people who have seen their best days, and whose thoughts are with the past and not the present. She participated in all the vanities of the great world, went to balls, where she sat in a corner, painted and dressed in old-fashioned style, like a deformed but indispensable ornament of the ball-room; all the guests on entering approached her and made a profound bow, as if in accordance with a set ceremony, but after that nobody took any further notice of her. She received the whole town at her house, and observed the strictest etiquette, although she could no longer recognise the faces of people. Her numerous domestics, growing fat and old in her ante-chamber and servants' hall, did just as they liked, and vied with each other in robbing the aged Countess in the most barefaced manner. Lizaveta Ivanovna was the martyr of the household. She made tea, and was reproached with using too much sugar; she read novels aloud to the Countess, and the faults of the author were visited upon her head; she accompanied the Countess in her walks, and was held answerable for the weather or the state of the pavement. A salary was attached to the post, but she very rarely received it, although she was expected to dress like everybody else, that is to say, like very few indeed. In society she played the most pitiable rôle. Everybody knew her, and nobody paid her any attention. At balls she danced only when a partner was wanted, and ladies would only take hold of her arm when it was necessary to lead her out of the room to attend to their dresses. She was very self-conscious, and felt her position keenly, and she looked about her with impatience for a deliverer to come to her rescue; but the young men, calculating in their giddiness, honoured her with but very little attention, although Lizaveta Ivanovna was a hundred times prettier than the bare-faced and cold-hearted marriageable girls around whom they hovered. Many a time did she quietly slink away from the glittering but wearisome drawing-room, to go and cry in her own poor little room, in which stood a screen, a chest of drawers, a looking-glass and a painted bedstead, and where a tallow candle burnt feebly in a copper candle-stick.

One morning—this was about two days after the evening party described at the beginning of this story, and a week previous to the scene at which we have just assisted—Lizaveta Ivanovna was seated near the window at her embroidery frame, when, happening to look out into the street, she caught sight of a young Engineer officer, standing motionless with his eyes fixed upon her window. She lowered her head and went on again with her work. About five minutes afterwards she looked out again—the young officer was still standing in the same place. Not being in the habit of coquetting with passing officers, she did not continue to gaze out into the street, but went on sewing for a couple of hours, without raising her head. Dinner was announced. She rose up and began to put her embroidery away, but glancing casually out of the window, she perceived the officer again. This seemed to her very strange. After dinner she went to the window with a certain feeling of uneasiness, but the officer was no longer there—and she thought no more about him.

A couple of days afterwards, just as she was stepping into the carriage with the Countess, she saw him again. He was standing close behind the door, with his face half-concealed by his fur collar, but his dark eyes sparkled beneath his cap. Lizaveta felt alarmed, though she knew not why, and she trembled as she seated herself in the carriage.

On returning home, she hastened to the window—the officer was standing in his accustomed place, with his eyes fixed upon her. She drew back, a prey to curiosity and agitated by a feeling which was quite new to her.

From that time forward not a day passed without the young officer making his appearance under the window at the customary hour, and between him and her there was established a sort of mute acquaintance. Sitting in her place at work, she used to feel his approach; and raising her head, she would look at him longer and longer each day. The young man seemed to be very grateful to her: she saw with the sharp eye of youth, how a sudden flush covered his pale cheeks each time that their glances met. After about a week she commenced to smile at him. . . .

When Tomsky asked permission of his grandmother the Countess to present one of his friends to her, the young girl's heart beat violently. But hearing that Narumov was not an Engineer, she regretted that by her thoughtless question, she had betrayed her secret to the volatile Tomsky.

Hermann was the son of a German who had become a naturalised Russian, and from whom he had inherited a small capital. Being firmly convinced of the necessity of preserving his independence, Hermann did not touch his private income, but lived on his pay, without allowing himself the slightest luxury. Moreover, he was reserved and ambitious, and his companions rarely had an opportunity of making merry at the expense of his extreme parsimony. He had strong passions and an ardent imagination, but his firmness of disposition preserved him from the ordinary errors of young men. Thus, though a gamester at heart, he never touched a card, for he considered his position did not allow him—as he said—"to risk the necessary in the hope of winning the superfluous," yet he would sit for nights together at the card table and follow with feverish anxiety the different turns of the game.

The story of the three cards had produced a powerful impression upon his imagination, and all night long he could think of nothing else. "If," he thought to himself the following evening, as he walked along the streets of St. Petersburg, "if the old Countess would but reveal her secret to me! if she would only tell me the names of the three winning cards. Why should I not try my fortune? I must get introduced to her and win her favour—become her lover. . . . But all that will take time, and she is eighty-seven years old: she might be dead in a week, in a couple of days even! . . . But the story itself: can it really be true? . . . No! Economy, temperance and industry: those are my winning cards; by means of them I shall be able to double my capital—increase it sevenfold, and procure for myself ease and independence."

Musing in this manner, he walked on until he found himself in one of the principal streets of St. Petersburg, in front of a house of antiquated architecture. The street was blocked with equipages; carriages one after the other drew up in front of the brilliantly illuminated doorway. At one moment there stepped out on to the pavement the well-shaped little foot of some young beauty, at another the heavy boot of a cavalry officer, and then the silk stockings and shoes of a member of the diplomatic world. Furs and cloaks passed in rapid succession before the gigantic porter at the entrance.

Hermann stopped. "Whose house is this?" he asked of the watchman at the corner.

"The Countess A——'s," replied the watchman.

Hermann started. The strange story of the three cards again presented itself to his imagination. He began walking up and down before the house, thinking of its owner and her strange secret. Returning late to his modest lodging, he could not go to sleep for a long time, and when at last he did doze off, he could dream of nothing but cards, green tables, piles of banknotes and heaps of ducats. He played one card after the other, winning uninterruptedly, and then he gathered up the gold and filled his pockets with the notes. When he woke up late the next morning, he sighed over the loss of his imaginary wealth, and then sallying out into the town, he found himself once more in front of the Countess's residence. Some unknown power seemed to have attracted him thither. He stopped and looked up at the windows. At one of these he saw a head with luxuriant black hair, which was bent down probably over some book or an embroidery frame. The head was raised. Herman saw a fresh complexion and a pair of dark eyes. That moment decided his fate.

III

Lizaveta Ivanovna had scarcely taken off her hat and cloak, when the Countess sent for her and again ordered her to get the carriage ready. The vehicle drew up before the door, and they prepared to take their seats. Just at the moment when two footmen were assisting the old lady to enter the carriage, Lizaveta saw her Engineer standing close beside the wheel; he grasped her hand; alarm caused her to lose her presence of mind, and the young man disappeared—but not before he had left a letter between her fingers. She concealed it in her glove, and during the whole of the drive she neither saw nor heard anything. It was the custom of the Countess, when out for an airing in her carriage, to be constantly asking such questions as: "Who was that person that met us just now? What is the name of this bridge? What is written on that signboard?" On this occasion, however, Lizaveta returned such vague and absurd answers, that the Countess became angry with her.

"What is the matter with you, my dear?" she exclaimed. "Have you taken leave of your senses, or what is it? Do you not hear me or understand what I say? . . . Heaven be thanked, I am still in my right mind and speak plainly enough!"

Lizaveta Ivanovna did not hear her. On returning home she ran to her room, and drew the letter out of her glove: it was not sealed. Lizaveta read it. The letter contained a declaration of love; it was tender, respectful, and copied word for word from a German novel. But Lizaveta did not know anything of the German language, and she was quite delighted.

For all that, the letter caused her to feel exceedingly uneasy. For the first time in her life she was entering into secret and confidential relations with a young man. His boldness alarmed her. She reproached herself for her imprudent behaviour, and knew not what to do. Should she cease to sit at the window and, by assuming an appearance of indifference towards him, put a check upon the young officer's desire for further acquaintance with her? Should she send his letter back to him, or should she answer him in a cold and decided manner? There was nobody to whom she could turn in her perplexity, for she had neither female friend nor adviser. . . . . At length she resolved to reply to him.

She sat down at her little writing-table, took pen and paper, and began to think. Several times she began her letter, and then tore it up: the way she had expressed herself seemed to her either too inviting or too cold and decisive. At last she succeeded in writing a few lines with which she felt satisfied.

"I am convinced," she wrote, "that your intentions are honourable, and that you do not wish to offend me by any imprudent behaviour, but our acquaintance must not begin in such a manner. I return you your letter, and I hope that I shall never have any cause to complain of this undeserved slight."

The next day, as soon as Hermann made his appearance, Lizaveta rose from her embroidery, went into the drawing-room, opened the ventilator and threw the letter into the street, trusting that the young officer would have the perception to pick it up.

Hermann hastened forward, picked it up and then repaired to a confectioner's shop. Breaking the seal of the envelope, he found inside it his own letter and Lizaveta's reply. He had expected this, and he returned home, his mind deeply occupied with his intrigue.

Three days afterwards, a bright-eyed young girl from a milliner's establishment brought Lizaveta a letter. Lizaveta opened it with great uneasiness, fearing that it was a demand for money, when suddenly she recognised Hermann's hand-writing.

"You have made a mistake, my dear," said she. "This letter is not for me."

"Oh, yes, it is for you," replied the girl, smiling very knowingly. "Have the goodness to read it."

Lizaveta glanced at the letter. Hermann requested an interview.

"It cannot be," she cried, alarmed at the audacious request, and the manner in which it was made. "This letter is certainly not for me."

And she tore it into fragments.

"If the letter was not for you, why have you torn it up?" said the girl. "I should have given it back to the person who sent it."

"Be good enough, my dear," said Lizaveta, disconcerted by this remark, "not to bring me any more letters in the future, and tell the person who sent you that he ought to be ashamed. . . ."

But Hermann was not the man to be thus put off. Every day Lizaveta received from him a letter, sent now in this way, now in that. They were no longer translated from the German. Hermann wrote them under the inspiration of passion, and spoke in his own language, and they bore full testimony to the inflexibility of his desire and the disordered condition of his uncontrollable imagination. Lizaveta no longer thought of sending them back to him: she became intoxicated with them and began to reply to them, and little by little her answers became longer and more affectionate. At last she threw out of the window to him the following letter:

"This evening there is going to be a ball at the Embassy. The Countess will be there. We shall remain until two o'clock. You have now an opportunity of seeing me alone. As soon as the Countess is gone, the servants will very probably go out, and there will be nobody left but the Swiss, but he usually goes to sleep in his lodge. Come about half-past eleven. Walk straight upstairs. If you meet anybody in the ante-room, ask if the Countess is at home. You will be told 'No,' in which case there will be nothing left for you to do but to go away again. But it is most probable that you will meet nobody. The maidservants will all be together in one room. On leaving the ante-room, turn to the left, and walk straight on until you reach the Countess's bedroom. In the bedroom, behind a screen, you will find two doors: the one on the right leads to a cabinet, which the Countess never enters; the one on the left leads to a corridor, at the end of which is a little winding staircase; this leads to my room."

Hermann trembled like a tiger, as he waited for the appointed time to arrive. At ten o'clock in the evening he was already in front of the Countess's house. The weather was terrible; the wind blew with great violence; the sleety snow fell in large flakes; the lamps emitted a feeble light, the streets were deserted; from time to time a sledge, drawn by a sorry-looking hack, passed by, on the lookout for a belated passenger. Hermann was enveloped in a thick overcoat, and felt neither wind nor snow.

At last the Countess's carriage drew up. Hermann saw two footmen carry out in their arms the bent form of the old lady, wrapped in sable fur, and immediately behind her, clad in a warm mantle, and with her head ornamented with a wreath of fresh flowers, followed Lizaveta. The door was closed. The carriage rolled away heavily through the yielding snow. The porter shut the street-door; the windows became dark.

Hermann began walking up and down near the deserted house; at length he stopped under a lamp, and glanced at his watch: it was twenty minutes past eleven. He remained standing under the lamp, his eyes fixed upon the watch, impatiently waiting for the remaining minutes to pass. At half-past eleven precisely, Hermann ascended the steps of the house, and made his way into the brightly-illuminated vestibule. The porter was not there. Hermann hastily ascended the staircase, opened the door of the ante-room and saw a footman sitting asleep in an antique chair by the side of a lamp. With a light firm step Hermann passed by him. The drawing-room and dining-room were in darkness, but a feeble reflection penetrated thither from the lamp in the ante-room.

Hermann reached the Countess's bedroom. Before a shrine, which was full of old images, a golden lamp was burning. Faded stuffed chairs and divans with soft cushions stood in melancholy symmetry around the room, the walls of which were hung with China silk. On one side of the room hung two portraits painted in Paris by Madame Lebrun. One of these represented a stout, red-faced man of about forty years of age in a bright-green uniform and with a star upon his breast; the other—a beautiful young woman, with an aquiline nose, forehead curls and a rose in her powdered hair. In the corners stood porcelain shepherds and shepherdesses, dining-room clocks from the workshop of the celebrated Lefroy, bandboxes, roulettes, fans and the various playthings for the amusement of ladies that were in vogue at the end of the last century, when Montgolfier's balloons and Mesmer's magnetism were the rage. Hermann stepped behind the screen. At the back of it stood a little iron bedstead; on the right was the door which led to the cabinet; on the left—the other which led to the corridor. He opened the latter, and saw the little winding staircase which led to the room of the poor companion. . . . But he retraced his steps and entered the dark cabinet.

The time passed slowly. All was still. The clock in the drawing-room struck twelve; the strokes echoed through the room one after the other, and everything was quiet again. Hermann stood leaning against the cold stove. He was calm; his heart beat regularly, like that of a man resolved upon a dangerous but inevitable undertaking. One o'clock in the morning struck; then two; and he heard the distant noise of carriage-wheels. An involuntary agitation took possession of him. The carriage drew near and stopped. He heard the sound of the carriage-steps being let down. All was bustle within the house. The servants were running hither and thither, there was a confusion of voices, and the rooms were lit up. Three antiquated chambermaids entered the bedroom, and they were shortly afterwards followed by the Countess who, more dead than alive, sank into a Voltaire armchair. Hermann peeped through a chink. Lizaveta Ivanovna passed close by him, and he heard her hurried steps as she hastened up the little spiral staircase. For a moment his heart was assailed by something like a pricking of conscience, but the emotion was only transitory, and his heart became petrified as before.

The Countess began to undress before her looking-glass. Her rose-bedecked cap was taken off, and then her powdered wig was removed from off her white and closely-cut hair. Hairpins fell in showers around her. Her yellow satin dress, brocaded with silver, fell down at her swollen feet.

Hermann was a witness of the repugnant mysteries of her toilette; at last the Countess was in her night-cap and dressing-gown, and in this costume, more suitable to her age, she appeared less hideous and deformed.

Like all old people in general, the Countess suffered from sleeplessness. Having undressed, she seated herself at the window in a Voltaire armchair and dismissed her maids. The candles were taken away, and once more the room was left with only one lamp burning in it. The Countess sat there looking quite yellow, mumbling with her flaccid lips and swaying to and fro. Her dull eyes expressed complete vacancy of mind, and, looking at her, one would have thought that the rocking of her body was not a voluntary action of her own, but was produced by the action of some concealed galvanic mechanism.

Suddenly the death-like face assumed an inexplicable expression. The lips ceased to tremble, the eyes became animated: before the Countess stood an unknown man.

"Do not be alarmed, for Heaven's sake, do not be alarmed!" said he in a low but distinct voice. "I have no intention of doing you any harm, I have only come to ask a favour of you."

The old woman looked at him in silence, as if she had not heard what he had said. Hermann thought that she was deaf, and, bending down towards her ear, he repeated what he had said. The aged Countess remained silent as before.

"You can insure the happiness of my life," continued Hermann, "and it will cost you nothing. I know that you can name three cards in order—"

Hermann stopped. The Countess appeared now to understand what he wanted; she seemed as if seeking for words to reply.

"It was a joke," she replied at last. "I assure you it was only a joke."

"There is no joking about the matter," replied Hermann angrily. "Remember Chaplitzky, whom you helped to win."

The Countess became visibly uneasy. Her features expressed strong emotion, but they quickly resumed their former immobility.

"Can you not name me these three winning cards?" continued Hermann.

The Countess remained silent; Hermann continued:

"For whom are you preserving your secret? For your grandsons? They are rich enough without it; they do not know the worth of money. Your cards would be of no use to a spendthrift. He who cannot preserve his paternal inheritance will die in want, even though he had a demon at his service. I am not a man of that sort; I know the value of money. Your three cards will not be thrown away upon me. Come!" . . .

He paused and tremblingly awaited her reply. The Countess remained silent; Hermann fell upon his knees.

"If your heart has ever known the feeling of love," said he, "if you remember its rapture, if you have ever smiled at the cry of your new-born child, if any human feeling has ever entered into your breast, I entreat you by the feelings of a wife, a lover, a mother, by all that is most sacred in life, not to reject my prayer. Reveal to me your secret. Of what use is it to you? . . . Maybe it is connected with some terrible sin, with the loss of eternal salvation, with some bargain with the devil. . . . Reflect,—you are old; you have not long to live—I am ready to take your sins upon my soul. Only reveal to me your secret. Remember that the happiness of a man is in your hands, that not only I, but my children, and grandchildren will bless your memory and reverence you as a saint. . . ."

The old Countess answered not a word.

Hermann rose to his feet.

"You old hag!" he exclaimed, grinding his teeth, "then I will make you answer!"

With these words he drew a pistol from his pocket.

At the sight of the pistol, the Countess for the second time exhibited strong emotion. She shook her head and raised her hands as if to protect herself from the shot. . . . then she fell backwards and remained motionless.

"Come, an end to this childish nonsense!" said Hermann, taking hold of her hand. "I ask you for the last time: will you tell me the names of your three cards, or will you not?"

The Countess made no reply. Hermann perceived that she was dead.

IV

Lizaveta Ivanovna was sitting in her room, still in her ball dress, lost in deep thought. On returning home, she had hastily dismissed the chambermaid who very reluctantly came forward to assist her, saying that she would undress herself, and with a trembling heart had gone up to her own room, expecting to find Hermann there, but yet hoping not to find him. At the first glance she convinced herself that he was not there, and she thanked her fate for having prevented him keeping the appointment. She sat down without undressing, and began to recall to mind all the circumstances which in so short a time had carried her so far. It was not three weeks since the time when she first saw the young officer from the window—and yet she was already in correspondence with him, and he had succeeded in inducing her to grant him a nocturnal interview! She knew his name only through his having written it at the bottom of some of his letters; she had never spoken to him, had never heard his voice, and had never heard him spoken of until that evening. But, strange to say, that very evening at the ball, Tomsky, being piqued with the young Princess Pauline N——, who, contrary to her usual custom, did not flirt with him, wished to revenge himself by assuming an air of indifference: he therefore engaged Lizaveta Ivanovna and danced an endless mazurka with her. During the whole of the time he kept teasing her about her partiality for Engineer officers; he assured her that he knew far more than she imagined, and some of his jests were so happily aimed, that Lizaveta thought several times that her secret was known to him.

"From whom have you learnt all this?" she asked, smiling.

"From a friend of a person very well known to you," replied Tomsky, "from a very distinguished man."

"And who is this distinguished man?"

"His name is Hermann."

Lizaveta made no reply; but her hands and feet lost all sense of feeling.

"This Hermann," continued Tomsky, "is a man of romantic personality. He has the profile of a Napoleon, and the soul of a Mephistopheles. I believe that he has at least three crimes upon his conscience. . . . How pale you have become!"

"I have a headache . . . But what did this Hermann—or whatever his name is—tell you?"

"Hermann is very much dissatisfied with his friend: he says that in his place he would act very differently . . . I even think that Hermann himself has designs upon you; at least, he listens very attentively to all that his friend has to say about you."

"And where has he seen me?"

"In church, perhaps; or on the parade—God alone knows where. It may have been in your room, while you were asleep, for there is nothing that he—"

Three ladies approaching him with the question: *"oubli ou regret?"*[2] interrupted the conversation, which had become so tantalisingly interesting to Lizaveta.

The lady chosen by Tomsky was the Princess Pauline herself. She succeeded in effecting a reconciliation with him during the numerous turns of the dance, after which he conducted her to her chair. On returning to his place, Tomsky thought no more either of Hermann or Lizaveta. She longed to renew the interrupted conversation, but the mazurka came to an end, and shortly afterwards the old Countess took her departure.

Tomsky's words were nothing more than the customary small talk of the dance, but they sank deep into the soul of the young dreamer. The portrait, sketched by Tomsky, coincided with the picture she had formed within her own mind, and thanks to the latest romances, the ordinary countenance of her admirer became invested with attributes capable of alarming her and fascinating her imagination at the same time. She was now sitting with her bare arms crossed and with her head, still adorned with flowers,

---

[2] Oblivion or regret.

sunk upon her uncovered bosom. Suddenly the door opened and Hermann entered. She shuddered.

"Where were you?" she asked in a terrified whisper.

"In the old Countess's bedroom," replied Hermann. "I have just left her. The Countess is dead."

"My God! What do you say?"

"And I am afraid," added Hermann, "that I am the cause of her death."

Lizaveta looked at him, and Tomsky's words found an echo in her soul: "This man has at least three crimes upon his conscience!" Hermann sat down by the window near her, and related all that had happened.

Lizaveta listened to him in terror. So all those passionate letters, those ardent desires, this bold obstinate pursuit—all this was not love! Money— that was what his soul yearned for! She could not satisfy his desire and make him happy! The poor girl had been nothing but the blind tool of a robber, of the murderer of her aged benefactress! . . . She wept bitter tears of agonised repentance. Hermann gazed at her in silence: his heart, too, was a prey to violent emotion, but neither the tears of the poor girl, nor the wonderful charm of her beauty, enhanced by her grief, could produce any impression upon his hardened soul. He felt no pricking of conscience at the thought of the dead old woman. One thing only grieved him: the irreparable loss of the secret from which he had expected to obtain great wealth.

"You are a monster!" said Lizaveta at last.

"I did not wish for her death," replied Hermann. "My pistol was not loaded."

Both remained silent.

The day began to dawn. Lizaveta extinguished her candle: a pale light illumined her room. She wiped her tear-stained eyes and raised them towards Hermann: he was sitting near the window, with his arms crossed and with a fierce frown upon his forehead. In this attitude he bore a striking resemblance to the portrait of Napoleon. This resemblance struck Lizaveta even.

"How shall I get you out of the house?" said she at last. "I thought of conducting you down the secret staircase, but in that case it would be necessary to go through the Countess's bedroom, and I am afraid."

"Tell me how to find this secret staircase—I will go alone."

Lizaveta arose, took from her drawer a key, handed it to Hermann and gave him the necessary instructions. Hermann pressed her cold, limp hand, kissed her bowed head, and left the room.

He descended the winding staircase, and once more entered the Countess's bedroom. The dead old lady sat as if petrified; her face expressed profound tranquillity. Hermann stopped before her, and gazed long and earnestly at her, as if he wished to convince himself of the terrible reality; at last he

entered the cabinet, felt behind the tapestry for the door, and then began
to descend the dark staircase, filled with strange emotions. "Down this
very staircase," thought he, "perhaps coming from the very same room, and
at this very same hour sixty years ago, there may have glided, in an embroidered coat, with his hair dressed *à l'oiseau royal* and pressing to his
heart his three-cornered hat, some young gallant, who has long been moulder-
ing in the grave, but the heart of his aged mistress has only today ceased
to beat. . . ."

At the bottom of the staircase Hermann found a door, which he opened
with a key, and then traversed a corridor which conducted him into the
street.

V

Three days after the fatal night, at nine o'clock in the morning, Hermann repaired to the Convent of ———, where the last honours were to be
paid to the mortal remains of the old Countess. Although feeling no remorse,
he could not altogether stifle the voice of conscience, which said to him:
"You are the murderer of the old woman!" In spite of his entertaining very
little religious belief, he was exceedingly superstitious; and believing that
the dead Countess might exercise an evil influence on his life, he resolved
to be present at her obsequies in order to implore her pardon.

The church was full. It was with difficulty that Hermann made his way
through the crowd of people. The coffin was placed upon a rich catafalque
beneath a velvet baldachin. The deceased Countess lay within it, with her
hands crossed upon her breast, with a lace cap upon her head and dressed in
a white satin robe. Around the catafalque stood the members of her household: the servants in black *caftans*, with armorial ribbons upon their shoulders, and candles in their hands; the relatives—children, grandchildren,
and great-grandchildren—in deep mourning.

Nobody wept; tears would have been *une affectation*. The Countess was so
old, that her death could have surprised nobody, and her relatives had long
looked upon her as being out of the world. A famous preacher pronounced
the funeral sermon. In simple and touching words he described the peaceful
passing away of the righteous, who had passed long years in calm prep-
aration for a Christian end. "The angel of death found her," said the
orator, "engaged in pious meditation and waiting for the midnight
bridegroom."

The service concluded amidst profound silence. The relatives went forward first to take farewell of the corpse. Then followed the numerous guests,
who had come to render the last homage to her who for so many years had
been a participator in their frivolous amusements. After these followed the
members of the Countess's household. The last of these was an old woman

of the same age as the deceased. Two young women led her forward by the hand. She had not strength enough to bow down to the ground—she merely shed a few tears and kissed the cold hand of her mistress.

Hermann now resolved to approach the coffin. He knelt down upon the cold stones and remained in that position for some minutes; at last he arose, as pale as the deceased Countess herself; he ascended the steps of the catafalque and bent over the corpse. . . . At that moment it seemed to him that the dead woman darted a mocking look at him and winked with one eye. Hermann started back, took a false step and fell to the ground. Several persons hurried forward and raised him up. At the same moment Lizaveta Ivanovna was borne fainting into the porch of the church. This episode disturbed for some minutes the solemnity of the gloomy ceremony. Among the congregation arose a deep murmur, and a tall thin chamberlain, a near relative of the deceased, whispered in the ear of an Englishman who was standing near him, that the young officer was a natural son of the Countess, to which the Englishman coldly replied: "Oh!"

During the whole of that day, Hermann was strangely excited. Repairing to an out-of-the-way restaurant to dine, he drank a great deal of wine, contrary to his usual custom, in the hope of deadening his inward agitation. But the wine only served to excite his imagination still more. On returning home, he threw himself upon his bed without undressing, and fell into a deep sleep.

When he woke up it was already night, and the moon was shining into the room. He looked at his watch: it was a quarter to three. Sleep had left him; he sat down upon his bed and thought of the funeral of the old Countess.

At that moment somebody in the street looked in at his window, and immediately passed on again. Hermann paid no attention to this incident. A few moments afterwards he heard the door of his ante-room open. Hermann thought that it was his orderly, drunk as usual, returning from some nocturnal expedition, but presently he heard footsteps that were unknown to him: somebody was walking softly over the floor in slippers. The door opened, and a woman dressed in white, entered the room. Hermann mistook her for his old nurse, and wondered what could bring her there at that hour of the night. But the white woman glided rapidly across the room and stood before him—and Hermann recognised the Countess!

"I have come to you against my wish," she said in a firm voice, "but I have been ordered to grant your request. Three, seven, ace, will win for you if played in succession, but only on these conditions: that you do not play more than one card in twenty-four hours, and that you never play again during the rest of your life. I forgive you my death, on condition that you marry my companion, Lizaveta Ivanovna."

With these words she turned round very quietly, walked with a shuffling gait towards the door and disappeared. Hermann heard the street-door open and shut, and again he saw some one look in at him through the window.

For a long time Hermann could not recover himself. He then rose up and entered the next room. His orderly was lying asleep upon the floor, and he had much difficulty in waking him. The orderly was drunk as usual, and no information could be obtained from him. The street-door was locked. Hermann returned to his room, lit his candle, and wrote down all the details of his vision.

VI

Two fixed ideas can no more exist together in the moral world than two bodies can occupy one and the same place in the physical world. "Three, seven, ace," soon drove out of Hermann's mind the thought of the dead Countess. "Three, seven, ace," were perpetually running through his head and continually being repeated by his lips. If he saw a young girl, he would say: "How slender she is! quite like the three of hearts." If anybody asked: "What is the time?" he would reply: "Five minutes to seven." Every stout man that he saw reminded him of the ace. "Three, seven, ace" haunted him in his sleep, and assumed all possible shapes. The threes bloomed before him in the forms of magnificent flowers, the sevens were represented by Gothic portals, and the aces became transformed into gigantic spiders. One thought alone occupied his whole mind—to make a profitable use of the secret which he had purchased so dearly. He thought of applying for a furlough so as to travel abroad. He wanted to go to Paris and tempt fortune in some of the public gambling-houses that abounded there. Chance spared him all this trouble.

There was in Moscow a society of rich gamesters, presided over by the celebrated Chekalinsky, who had passed all his life at the card-table and had amassed millions, accepting bills of exchange for his winnings and paying his losses in ready money. His long experience secured for him the confidence of his companions, and his open house, his famous cook, and his agreeable and fascinating manners gained for him the respect of the public. He came to St. Petersburg. The young men of the capital flocked to his rooms, forgetting balls for cards, and preferring the emotions of faro to the seductions of flirting. Narumov conducted Hermann to Chekalinsky's residence.

They passed through a suite of magnificent rooms, filled with attentive domestics. The place was crowded. Generals and Privy Counsellors were playing at whist; young men were lolling carelessly upon the velvet-covered sofas, eating ices and smoking pipes. In the drawing-room, at the head of a long table, around which were assembled about a score of players, sat the master of the house keeping the bank. He was a man of about sixty years of age, of a very dignified appearance; his head was covered with silvery-white hair; his full, florid countenance expressed good-nature, and his eyes twinkled with a perpetual smile. Narumov introduced Hermann to him. Chekalinsky shook him by the hand in a friendly manner, requesting him not to stand on ceremony, and then went on dealing.

The game occupied some time. On the table lay more than thirty cards. Chekalinsky paused after each throw, in order to give the players time to arrange their cards and note down their losses, listened politely to their requests, and more politely still, put straight the corners of cards that some player's hand had chanced to bend. At last the game was finished. Chekalinsky shuffled the cards and prepared to deal again.

"Will you allow me to take a card?" said Hermann, stretching out his hand from behind a stout gentleman who was playing.

Chekalinsky smiled and bowed silently, as a sign of acquiescence. Narumov laughingly congratulated Hermann on his abjuration of that abstention from cards which he had practised for so long a period, and wished him a lucky beginning.

"Stake!" said Hermann, writing some figures with chalk on the back of his card.

"How much?" asked the banker, contracting the muscles of his eyes; "excuse me, I cannot see quite clearly."

"Forty-seven thousand rubles," replied Hermann.

At these words every head in the room turned suddenly round, and all eyes were fixed upon Hermann.

"He has taken leave of his senses!" thought Narumov.

"Allow me to inform you," said Chekalinsky, with his eternal smile, "that you are playing very high; nobody here has ever staked more than two hundred and seventy-five rubles at once."

"Very well," replied Hermann; "but do you accept my card or not?"

Chekalinsky bowed in token of consent.

"I only wish to observe," said he, "that although I have the greatest confidence in my friends, I can only play against ready money. For my own part, I am quite convinced that your word is sufficient, but for the sake of the order of the game, and to facilitate the reckoning up, I must ask you to put the money on your card."

Hermann drew from his pocket a bank-note and handed it to Chekalinsky, who, after examining it in a cursory manner, placed it on Hermann's card.

He began to deal. On the right a nine turned up, and on the left a three.

"I have won!" said Hermann, showing his card.

A murmur of astonishment arose among the players. Chekalinsky frowned, but the smile quickly returned to his face.

"Do you wish me to settle with you?" he said to Hermann.

"If you please," replied the latter.

Chekalinsky drew from his pocket a number of bank-notes and paid at once. Hermann took up his money and left the table. Narumov could not recover from his astonishment. Hermann drank a glass of lemonade and returned home.

The next evening, he again repaired to Chekalinsky's. The host was dealing. Hermann walked up to the table; the punters immediately made room for him. Chekalinsky greeted him with a gracious bow.

Hermann waited for the next deal, took a card and placed upon it his forty-seven thousand rubles, together with his winnings of the previous evening.

Chekalinsky began to deal. A knave turned up on the right, a seven on the left.

Hermann showed his seven.

There was a general exclamation. Chekalinsky was evidently ill at ease, but he counted out the ninety-four thousand rubles and handed them over to Hermann, who pocketed them in the coolest manner possible and immediately left the house.

The next evening Hermann appeared again at the table. Every one was expecting him. Ten generals and Privy Counsellors left their whist in order to watch such extraordinary play. The young officers quitted their sofas, and even the servants crowded into the room. All pressed round Hermann. The other players left off the game, impatient to see how it would end. Hermann stood at the table and prepared to play alone against the pale, but still smiling Chekalinsky. Each opened a pack of cards. Chekalinsky shuffled. Hermann took a card and covered it with a pile of bank-notes. It was like a duel. Deep silence reigned around.

Chekalinsky began to deal; his hands trembled. On the right a queen turned up, and on the left an ace.

"Ace has won!" cried Hermann, showing his card.

"Your queen has lost," said Chekalinsky, politely.

Hermann started; instead of an ace, there lay before him the queen of spades! He could not believe his eyes, nor could he understand how he had made such a mistake.

At that moment it seemed to him that the queen of spades smiled ironically and winked her eye at him. He was struck by her remarkable resemblance. . . .

"The old Countess!" he exclaimed, seized with terror.

Chekalinsky gathered up his winnings. For some time, Hermann remained perfectly motionless. When at last he left the table, there was a general commotion in the room.

"Splendidly done!" said the players. Chekalinsky shuffled the cards afresh, and the game went on as usual.

Hermann went out of his mind, and is now confined in room Number 17 of the Obukhov Hospital. He never answers any questions, but he constantly mutters with unusual rapidity: "Three, seven, ace!" "Three, seven, queen!"

Lizaveta Ivanovna has married a very amiable young man, a son of the former steward of the old Countess. He is in the service of the State somewhere, and is in receipt of a good income. Lizaveta is also supporting a poor relative.

Tomsky has been promoted to the rank of captain, and has become the husband of the Princess Pauline.

Questions for Discussion

1. To what extent is the whole story foreshadowed in the characters and events of Part I?

2. How are the Countess and Hermann contrasted? What is the point of this contrast?

3. Is Lizaveta brought into the story simply to further the plot or does she have some other function?

4. What is meant by Tomsky saying that Hermann has the "profile of a Napoleon, and the soul of a Mephistopheles"? In what sense could he be considered a dual personality? Does he actually have "three crimes" on his conscience? If so, what are they?

5. To what do you attribute Hermann's vision at the end of Part V? Is it introduced without cause from outside him or does it stem from within? In general how could the supernatural in the story be explained in natural terms?

6. Why is it appropriate that Hermann should go mad at the end of the story and Lizaveta should be "supporting a poor relative"?

Edgar Allan Poe (1809–1849)

William Wilson

> What say of it? what say conscience grim
> That spectre in my path?
> —Chamberlain's *Pharronida.*

Let me call myself, for the present, William Wilson. The fair page now lying before me need not be sullied with my real appellation. This has been already too much an object for the scorn—for the horror—for the detestation of my race. To the uttermost regions of the globe have not the indignant winds bruited its unparalleled infamy? Oh, outcast of all outcasts most abandoned!—to the earth art thou not for ever dead? to its honors, to its flowers, to its golden aspirations?—and a cloud, dense, dismal, and limitless, does it not hang eternally between thy hopes and heaven?

I would not, if I could, here or to-day, embody a record of my later years of unspeakable misery, and unpardonable crime. This epoch—these later years—took unto themselves a sudden elevation in turpitude, whose origin alone it is my present purpose to assign. Men usually grow base by degrees. From me, in an instant, all virtue dropped bodily as a mantle. From comparatively trivial wickedness I passed, with the stride of a giant, into more than the enormities of an Elah-Gabalus. What chance—what one event brought this evil thing to pass, bear with me while I relate. Death approaches; and the shadow which foreruns him has thrown a softening influence over my spirit. I long, in passing through the dim valley, for the sympathy—I had nearly said for the pity—of my fellow men. I would fain have them believe that I have been, in some measure, the slave of circumstances beyond human control. I would wish them to seek out for me, in the details I am about to give, some little oasis of *fatality* amid a wilderness of error. I would have them allow—what they cannot refrain from allowing—that, although temptation may have erewhile existed as great, man was never *thus*, at least, tempted before—certainly, never *thus* fell. And is it therefore that he has never thus suffered? Have I not indeed been living in a dream? And am I not now dying a victim to the horror and the mystery of the wildest of all sublunary visions?

I am the descendant of a race whose imaginative and easily excitable temperament has at all times rendered them remarkable; and, in my earliest infancy, I gave evidence of having fully inherited the family character. As I advanced in years it was more strongly developed; becoming, for many reasons, a cause of serious disquietude to my friends, and of positive injury to myself. I grew self-willed, addicted to the wildest caprices, and a prey to the most ungovernable passions. Weak-minded, and beset with constitutional infirmities akin to my own, my parents could do but little to check the evil propensities which distinguished me. Some feeble and ill-directed efforts resulted in complete failure on their part, and, of course, in total triumph on mine. Thenceforward my voice was a household law; and at an age when few children have abandoned their leading-strings, I was left to the guidance of my own will, and became, in all but name, the master of my own actions.

My earliest recollections of a school-life are connected with a large, rambling, Elizabethan house, in a misty-looking village of England, where were a vast number of gigantic and gnarled trees, and where all the houses were excessively ancient. In truth, it was a dream-like and spirit-soothing place, that venerable old town. At this moment, in fancy, I feel the refreshing chilliness of its deeply-shadowed avenues, inhale the fragrance of its thousand shrubberies, and thrill anew with undefinable delight, at the deep hollow note of the church-bell, breaking, each hour, with sullen and sudden roar, upon the stillness of the dusky atmosphere in which the fretted Gothic steeple lay imbedded and asleep.

It gives me, perhaps, as much of pleasure as I can now in any manner experience, to dwell upon minute recollections of the school and its concerns. Steeped in misery as I am—misery, alas! only too real—I shall be pardoned for seeking relief, however slight and temporary, in the weakness of a few rambling details. These, moreover, utterly trivial, and even ridiculous in themselves, assume, to my fancy, adventitious importance, as connected with a period and a locality when and where I recognise the first ambiguous monitions of the destiny which afterwards so fully overshadowed me. Let me then remember.

The house, I have said, was old and irregular. The grounds were extensive, and a high and solid brick wall, topped with a bed of mortar and broken glass, encompassed the whole. This prison-like rampart formed the limit of our domain; beyond it we saw but thrice a week—once every Saturday afternoon, when, attended by two ushers, we were permitted to take brief walks in a body through some of the neighboring fields—and twice during Sunday, when we were paraded in the same formal manner to the morning and evening service in the one church of the village. Of this church the principal of our school was pastor. With how deep a spirit of wonder and perplexity was I wont to regard him from our remote pew in the gallery, as, with step solemn and slow, he ascended the pulpit! This reverend man, with countenance so demurely benign, with robes so glossy and so clerically flowing, with wig so minutely powdered, so rigid and so vast,—could this be he who, of late, with sour visage, and in snuffy habiliments, administered, ferrule in hand, the Draconian Laws of the academy? Oh, gigantic paradox, too utterly monstrous for solution!

At an angle of the ponderous wall frowned a more ponderous gate. It was riveted and studded with iron bolts, and surmounted with jagged iron spikes. What impressions of deep awe did it inspire! It was never opened save for the three periodical egressions and ingressions already mentioned; then, in every creak of its mighty hinges, we found a plenitude of mystery— a world of matter for solemn remark, or for more solemn meditation.

The extensive enclosure was irregular in form, having many capacious recesses. Of these, three or four of the largest constituted the play-ground. It was level, and covered with fine hard gravel. I well remember it had no trees, nor benches, nor any thing similar within it. Of course it was in the rear of the house. In front lay a small parterre, planted with box and other shrubs; but through this sacred division we passed only upon rare occasions indeed—such as a first advent to school or final departure thence, or perhaps, when a parent or friend having called for us, we joyfully took our way home for the Christmas or Midsummer holydays.

But the house!—how quaint an old building was this!—to me how veritably a palace of enchantment! There was really no end to its windings— to its incomprehensible subdivisions. It was difficult, at any given time, to say with certainty upon which of its two stories one happened to be. From each room to every other there were sure to be found three or four steps either in ascent or descent. Then the lateral branches were innumerable— inconceivable—and so returning in upon themselves, that our most exact ideas in regard to the whole mansion were not very far different from those with which we pondered upon infinity. During the five years of my residence here, I was never able to ascertain with precision, in what remote locality lay the little sleeping apartment assigned to myself and some eighteen or twenty other scholars.

The school-room was the largest in the house—I could not help thinking, in the world. It was very long, narrow, and dismally low, with pointed Gothic windows and a ceiling of oak. In a remote and terror-inspiring angle was a square enclosure of eight or ten feet, comprising the *sanctum*, "during hours," of our principal, the Reverend Dr. Bransby. It was a solid structure, with massy door, sooner than open which in the absence of the "Dominie," we would all have willingly perished by the *peine forte et dure*.[1] In other angles were two other similar boxes, far less reverenced, indeed, but still greatly matters of awe. One of these was the pulpit of the "classical" usher, one of the "English and mathematical." Interspersed about the room, crossing and re-crossing in endless irregularity, were innumerable benches and desks, black, ancient, and time-worn, piled desperately with much-bethumbed books, and so beseamed with initial letters, names at full length, grotesque figures, and other multiplied efforts of the knife, as to have entirely lost what little of original form might have been their portion in days long departed. A huge bucket with water stood at one extremity of the room, and a clock of stupendous dimensions at the other.

Encompassed by the massy walls of this venerable academy, I passed, yet not in tedium or disgust, the years of the third lustrum of my life. The teeming brain of childhood requires no external world of incident to occupy or amuse it; and the apparently dismal monotony of a school was replete with more intense excitement than my riper youth has derived from luxury, or my full manhood from crime. Yet I must believe that my first mental development had in it much of the uncommon—even much of the *outre*.[2] Upon mankind at large the events of very early existence rarely leave in mature age any definite impression. All is gray shadow—a weak and irregular remembrance —an indistinct regathering of feeble pleasures and phantasmagoric pains. With me this is not so. In childhood I must have felt with the energy of a man what I now find stamped upon memory in lines as vivid, as deep, and as durable as the *exergues*[3] of the Carthaginian medals.

Yet in fact—in the fact of the world's view—how little was there to remember! The morning's awakening, the nightly summons to bed; the connings, the recitations; the periodical half-holidays, and perambulations; the play-ground, with its broils, its pastimes, its intrigues;—these, by a mental sorcery long forgotten, were made to involve a wilderness of sensation, a world of rich incident, a universe of varied emotion, of excitement the most passionate and spirit-stirring. *"Oh, le bon temps, que ce siècle de fer!"*[4]

In truth, the ardor, the enthusiasm, and the imperiousness of my disposition, soon rendered me a marked character among my schoolmates, and by slow, but natural gradations, gave me an ascendency over all not greatly older than myself;—over all with a single exception. This exception was found in the person of a scholar, who, although no relation, bore the same Christian and surname as myself;—a circumstance, in fact, little remarkable; for, notwithstanding a noble descent, mine was one of those everyday

---

1 Difficulty and suffering.
2 That which goes beyond.
3 The space beneath the base line on a medal.
4 "Oh, what a good time is this iron century!"

appellations which seem, by prescriptive right, to have been, time out of mind, the common property of the mob. In this narrative I have therefore designated myself as William Wilson,—a fictitious title not very dissimilar to the real. My namesake alone, of those who in school-phraseology constituted "our set," presumed to compete with me in the studies of the class— in the sports and broils of the play-ground—to refuse implicit belief in my assertions, and submission to my will—indeed, to interfere with my arbitrary dictation in any respect whatsoever. If there is on earth a supreme and unqualified despotism, it is the despotism of a master-mind in boyhood over the less energetic spirits of its companions.

Wilson's rebellion was to me a source of the greatest embarrassment; the more so as, in spite of the bravado with which in public I made a point of treating him and his pretensions, I secretly felt that I feared him, and could not help thinking the equality which he maintained so easily with myself, a proof of his true superiority; since not to be overcome cost me a perpetual struggle. Yet this superiority—even this equality—was in truth acknowledged by no one but myself; our associates, by some unaccountable blindness, seemed not even to suspect it. Indeed, his competition, his resistance, and especially his impertinent and dogged interference with my purposes, were not more pointed than private. He appeared to be destitute alike of the ambition which urged, and of the passionate energy of mind which enabled me to excel. In his rivalry he might have been supposed actuated solely by a whimsical desire to thwart, astonish, or mortify myself; although there were times when I could not help observing, with a feeling made up of wonder, abasement, and pique, that he mingled with his injuries, his insults, or his contradictions, a certain most inappropriate, and assuredly most unwelcome *affectionateness* of manner. I could only conceive this singular behavior to arise from a consummate self-conceit assuming the vulgar airs of patronage and protection.

Perhaps it was this latter trait in Wilson's conduct, conjoined with our identity of name, and the mere accident of our having entered the school upon the same day, which set afloat the notion that we were brothers, among the senior classes in the academy. These do not usually inquire with much strictness into the affairs of their juniors. I have before said, or should have said, that Wilson was not, in the most remote degree, connected with my family. But assuredly if we *had* been brothers we must have been twins; for, after leaving Dr. Bransby's, I casually learned that my namesake was born on the nineteenth of January, 1813—and this is a somewhat remarkable coincidence; for the day is precisely that of my own nativity.

It may seem strange that in spite of the continual anxiety occasioned me by the rivalry of Wilson, and his intolerable spirit of contradiction, I could not bring myself to hate him altogether. We had, to be sure, nearly every day a quarrel in which, yielding me publicly the palm of victory, he, in some manner, contrived to make me feel that it was he who had deserved it; yet a sense of pride on my part, and a veritable dignity on his own, kept us always upon what are called "speaking terms," while there were many points of strong congeniality in our tempers, operating to awake in me a sentiment which our position alone, perhaps, prevented from ripening into friendship. It is difficult, indeed, to define, or even to describe, my real feelings towards him. They formed a motley and heterogeneous admixture; —some petulant animosity, which was not yet hatred, some esteem, more respect, much fear, with a world of uneasy curiosity. To the moralist it will be unnecessary to say, in addition, that Wilson and myself were the most inseparable of companions.

It was no doubt the anomalous state of affairs existing between us, which turned all my attacks upon him, (and they were many, either open or covert) into the channel of banter or practical joke (giving pain while assuming the aspect of mere fun) rather than into a more serious and determined hostility. But my endeavors on this head were by no means uniformly successful, even when my plans were the most wittily concocted; for my namesake had much about him, in character, of that unassuming and quiet austerity which, while enjoying the poignancy of its own jokes, has no heel of Achilles in itself, and absolutely refuses to be laughed at. I could find, indeed, but one vulnerable point, and that, lying in a personal peculiarity, arising, perhaps, from constitutional disease, would have been spared by any antagonist less at his wit's end than myself;—my rival had a weakness in the faucial or guttural organs, which precluded him from raising his voice at any time *above a very low whisper*. Of this defect I did not fail to take what poor advantage lay in my power.

Wilson's retaliations in kind were many; and there was one form of his practical wit that disturbed me beyond measure. How his sagacity first discovered at all that so petty a thing would vex me, is a question I never could solve; but having discovered, he habitually practised the annoyance. I had always felt aversion to my uncourtly patronymic, and its very common, if not plebeian prænomen. The words were venom in my ears; and when, upon the day of my arrival, a second William Wilson came also to the academy, I felt angry with him for bearing the name, and doubly disgusted with the name because a stranger bore it, who would be the cause of its twofold repetition, who would be constantly in my presence, and whose concerns, in the ordinary routine of the school business, must inevitably, on account of the detestable coincidence, be often confounded with my own.

The feeling of vexation thus engendered grew stronger with every circumstance tending to show resemblance, moral or physical, between my rival and myself. I had not then discovered the remarkable fact that we were of the same age; but I saw that we were of the same height, and I perceived that we were even singularly alike in general contour of person and outline of feature. I was galled, too, by the rumor touching a relationship, which had grown current in the upper forms. In a word, nothing could more seriously disturb me, (although I scrupulously concealed such disturbance,) than any allusion to a similarity of mind, person, or condition existing between us. But, in truth, I had no reason to believe that (with the exception of the matter of relationship, and in the case of Wilson himself,) this similarity had ever been made a subject of comment, or even observed at all by our schoolfellows. That *he* observed it in all its bearings, and as fixedly as I, was apparent; but that he could discover in such circumstances so fruitful a field of annoyance, can only be attributed, as I said before, to his more than ordinary penetration.

His cue, which was to perfect an imitation of myself, lay both in words and in actions; and most admirably did he play his part. My dress it was an easy matter to copy; my gait and general manner were, without difficulty, appropriated; in spite of his constitutional defect, even my voice did not escape him. My louder tones were, of course, unattempted, but then the key, it was identical; *and his singular whisper, it grew the very echo of my own.*

How greatly this most exquisite portraiture harassed me, (for it could not justly be termed a caricature,) I will not now venture to describe. I had but one consolation—in the fact that the imitation, apparently, was noticed by myself alone, and that I had to endure only the knowing and strangely sarcastic smiles of my namesake himself. Satisfied with having produced in my bosom the intended effect, he seemed to chuckle in secret over the sting he had inflicted, and was characteristically disregardful of the public applause which the success of his witty endeavors might have so easily elicited. That the school, indeed, did not feel his design, perceive its accomplishment, and participate in his sneer, was, for many anxious months, a riddle I could not resolve. Perhaps the *gradation* of his copy rendered it not so readily perceptible; or, more possibly, I owed my security to the masterly air of the copyist, who, disdaining the letter, (which in a painting is all the obtuse can see,) gave but the full spirit of his original for my individual contemplation and chagrin.

I have already more than once spoken of the disgusting air of patronage which he assumed toward me, and of his frequent officious interference with my will. This interference often took the ungracious character of advice; advice not openly given, but hinted or insinuated. I received it with a repugnance which gained strength as I grew in years. Yet, at this distant day, let me do him the simple justice to acknowledge that I can recall no occasion when the suggestions of my rival were on the side of those errors or follies so usual to his immature age and seeming inexperience; that his moral sense, at least, if not his general talents and worldly wisdom, was far keener than my own; and that I might, to-day, have been a better, and thus a happier man, had I less frequently rejected the counsels embodied in those meaning whispers which I then but too cordially hated and too bitterly despised.

As it was, I at length grew restive in the extreme under his distasteful supervision, and daily resented more and more openly what I considered his intolerable arrogance. I have said that, in the first years of our connexion as schoolmates, my feelings in regard to him might have been easily ripened into friendship; but, in the latter months of my residence at the academy, although the intrusion of his ordinary manner had, beyond doubt, in some measure abated, my sentiments, in nearly similar proportion, partook very much of positive hatred. Upon one occasion he saw this, I think, and afterwards avoided, or made a show of avoiding me.

It was about the same period, if I remember aright, that, in an altercation of violence with him, in which he was more than usually thrown off his guard, and spoke and acted with an openness of demeanor rather foreign to his nature, I discovered, or fancied I discovered, in his accent, his air, and general appearance, a something which first startled, and then deeply interested me, by bringing to mind dim visions of my earliest infancy—wild, confused and thronging memories of a time when memory herself was yet unborn. I cannot better describe the sensation which oppressed me, than by saying that I could with difficulty shake off the belief of my having been acquainted with the being who stood before me, at some epoch very long ago—some point of the past even infinitely remote. The delusion, however, faded rapidly as it came; and I mention it at all but to define the day of the last conversation I there held with my singular namesake.

The huge old house, with its countless subdivisions, had several large chambers communicating with each other, where slept the greater number of the students. There were, however, (as must necessarily happen in a building so awkwardly planned,) many little nooks or recesses, the odds and ends of the structure; and these the economic ingenuity of Dr. Bransby had also fitted up as dormitories; although, being the merest closets, they were capable of accommodating but a single individual. One of these small apartments was occupied by Wilson.

One night, about the close of my fifth year at the school, and immediately after the altercation just mentioned, finding every one wrapped in sleep, I arose from bed, and, lamp in hand, stole through a wilderness of narrow passages from my own bedroom to that of my rival. I had long been plotting one of those ill-natured pieces of practical wit at his expense in which I had hitherto been so uniformly unsuccessful. It was my intention, now, to put my scheme in operation, and I resolved to make him feel the whole extent of the malice with which I was imbued. Having reached his closet,

I noiselessly entered, leaving the lamp, with a shade over it, on the out-side. I advanced a step, and listened to the sound of his tranquil breathing. Assured of his being asleep, I returned, took the light, and with it again approached the bed. Close curtains were around it, which, in the prosecution of my plan, I slowly and quietly withdrew, when the bright rays fell vividly upon the sleeper, and my eyes, at the same moment, upon his countenance. I looked;—and a numbness, an iciness of feeling instantly pervaded my frame. My breast heaved, my knees tottered, my whole spirit became possessed with an objectless yet intolerable horror. Gasping for breath, I lowered the lamp in still nearer proximity to the face. Were these,—*these* the lineaments of William Wilson? I saw indeed, that they were his, but I shook as if with a fit of the ague, in fancying they were not. What *was* there about them to con-found me in this manner? I gazed;—while my brain reeled with a multitude of incoherent thoughts. Not thus he appeared—assuredly not *thus*—in the vivacity of his waking hours. The same name! the same contour of person! the same day of arrival at the academy! And then his dogged and meaning-less imitation of my gait, my voice, my habits, and my manner! Was it, in truth, within the bounds of human possibility, that *what I now saw* was the result, merely, of the habitual practice of this sarcastice imitation? Awe-stricken, and with a creeping shudder, I extinguished the lamp, passed silently from the chamber, and left, at once, the halls of that old academy, never to enter them again.

After a lapse of some months, spent at home in mere idleness, I found myself a student at Eton. The brief interval had been sufficient to enfeeble my remembrance of the events at Dr. Bransby's, or at least to effect a mate-rial change in the nature of the feelings with which I remembered them. The truth—the tragedy—of the drama was no more. I could now find room to doubt the evidence of my senses; and seldom called up the subject at all but with wonder at the extent of human credulity, and a smile at the vivid force of the imagination which I hereditarily possessed. Neither was this species of skepticism likely to be diminished by the character of the life I led at Eton. The vortex of thoughtless folly into which I there so imme-diately and so recklessly plunged, washed away all but the froth of my past hours, ingulfed at once every solid or serious impression, and left to memory only the veriest levities of a former existence.

I do not wish, however, to trace the course of my miserable profligacy here—a profligacy which set at defiance the laws, while it eluded the vigi-lance of the institution. Three years of folly, passed without profit, had but given me rooted habits of vice, and added, in a somewhat unusual degree, to my bodily stature, when, after a week of soulless dissipation, I invited a small party of the most dissolute students to a secret carousal in my cham-bers. We met at a late hour of the night; for our debaucheries were to be faithfully protracted until morning. The wine flowed freely, and there were not wanting other and perhaps more dangerous seductions; so that the gray dawn had already faintly appeared in the east, while our delirious extravagance was at its height. Madly flushed with cards and intoxication, I was in the act of insisting upon a toast of more than wonted profanity, when my attention was suddenly diverted by the violent, although partial unclosing of the door of the apartment, and by the eager voice of a servant from without. He said that some person, apparently in great haste, demanded to speak with me in the hall.

Wildly excited with wine, the unexpected interruption rather delighted than surprised me. I staggered forward at once, and a few steps brought me to the vestibule of the building. In this low and small room there hung no lamp; and now no light at all was admitted, save that of the exceedingly feeble dawn which made its way through the semicircular window. As I put my foot over the threshold I became aware of the figure of a youth about my own height, and habited in a white kerseymere morning frock, cut in the novel fashion of the one I myself wore at the moment. This the faint light enabled me to perceive; but the features of his face I could not distinguish. Upon my entering, he strode hurriedly up to me, and seizing me by the arm with a gesture of petulant impatience, whispered the words "William Wilson!" in my ear.

I grew perfectly sober in an instant.

There was that in the manner of the stranger, and in the tremulous shake of his uplifted finger, as he held it between my eyes and the light, which filled me with unqualified amazement; but it was not this which had so violently moved me. It was the pregnancy of solemn admonition in the singular, low, hissing utterance; and, above all, it was the character, the tone, *the key*, of those few, simple, and familiar, yet *whispered* syllables, which came with a thousand thronging memories of by-gone days, and struck upon my soul with the shock of a galvanic battery. Ere I could recover the use of my senses he was gone.

Although this event failed not of a vivid effect upon my disordered imagination, yet was it evanescent as vivid. For some weeks, indeed, I busied myself in earnest inquiry, or was wrapped in a cloud of morbid speculation. I did not pretend to disguise from my perception the identity of the singular individual who thus perseveringly interfered with my affairs, and harassed me with his insinuated counsel. But who and what was this Wilson?—and whence came he?—and what were his purposes? Upon neither of these points could I be satisfied—merely ascertaining, in regard to him, that a sudden accident in his family had caused his removal from Dr. Bransby's academy on the afternoon of the day in which I myself had eloped. But in a brief period I ceased to think upon the subject, my attention being all absorbed in a contemplated departure for Oxford. Thither I soon went, the uncalculating vanity of my parents furnishing me with an outfit and annual establishment, which would enable me to indulge at will in the luxury already so dear to my heart—to vie in profuseness of expenditure with the haughtiest heirs of the wealthiest earldoms in Great Britain.

Excited by such appliances to vice, my constitutional temperament broke forth with redoubled ardor, and I spurned even the common restraints of decency in the mad infatuation of my revels. But it were absurd to pause in the detail of my extravagance. Let it suffice, that among spendthrifts I out-Heroded Herod, and that, giving name to a multitude of novel follies, I added no brief appendix to the long catalogue of vices then usual in the most dissolute university of Europe.

It could hardly be credited, however, that I had, even here, so utterly fallen from the gentlemanly estate, as to seek acquaintance with the vilest arts of the gambler by profession, and, having become an adept in his despicable science, to practise it habitually as a means of increasing my already enormous income at the expense of the weak-minded among my fellow-collegians. Such, nevertheless, was the fact. And the very enormity of this offense against all manly and honorable sentiment proved, beyond doubt, the main if not the sole reason of the impunity with which it was committed. Who, indeed, among my most abandoned associates, would not rather have disputed the clearest evidence of his senses, than have suspected of such courses, the gay, the frank, the generous William Wilson—the noblest and most liberal commoner at Oxford—him whose follies (said his parasites) were but the follies of youth and unbridled fancy—whose errors but inimitable whim—whose darkest vice but a careless and dashing extravagance?

I had been now two years successfully busied in this way, when there came to the university a young *parvenu* nobleman, Glendinning—rich, said report, as Herodes Atticus—his riches, too, as easily acquired. I soon found him of weak intellect, and, of course, marked him as a fitting subject for my skill. I frequently engaged him in play, and contrived, with the gambler's usual art, to let him win considerable sums, the more effectually to entangle him in my snares. At length, my schemes being ripe, I met him (with the full intention that this meeting should be final and decisive) at the chambers of a fellow-commoner, (Mr. Preston,) equally intimate with both, but who, to do him justice, entertained not even a remote suspicion of my design. To give to this a better coloring, I had contrived to have assembled a party of some eight or ten, and was solicitously careful that the introduction of cards should appear accidental, and originate in the proposal of my contemplated dupe himself. To be brief upon a vile topic, none of the low

finesse was omitted, so customary upon similar occasions, that it is a just
matter for wonder how any are still found so besotted as to fall its victim.

We had protracted our sitting far into the night, and I had at length
effected the manœuvre of getting Glendinning as my sole antagonist. The
game, too, was my favorite *ecarte*.[5] The rest of the company interested in
the extent of our play, had abandoned their own cards, and were standing
around us as spectators. The *parvenu*, who had been induced by my artifices
in the early part of the evening, to drink deeply, now shuffled, dealt, or
played, with a wild nervousness of manner for which his intoxication, I
thought, might partially, but could not altogether account. In a very short
period he had become my debtor to a large amount, when, having taken
a long draught of port, he did precisely what I had been coolly anticipating—
he proposed to double our already extravagant stakes. With a well-feigned
show of reluctance, and not until after my repeated refusal had seduced him
into some angry words which gave a color of *pique* to my compliance, did
I finally comply. The result, of course, did but prove how entirely the prey
was in my toils; in less than an hour he had quadrupled his debt. For some
time his countenance had been losing the florid tinge lent it by the wine;
but now, to my astonishment, I perceived that it had grown to a pallor truly
fearful. I say, to my astonishment, Glendinning had been represented to my
eager inquiries as immeasurably wealthy; and the sums which he had as
yet lost, although in themselves vast, could not, I suppose, very seriously
annoy, much less so violently affect him. That he was overcome by the wine
just swallowed, was the idea which most readily presented itself; and, rather
with a view to the preservation of my own character in the eyes of my
associates, than from any less interested motive, I was about to insist,
peremptorily upon a discontinuance of the play, when some expressions at
my elbow from among the company, and an ejaculation evincing utter
despair on the part of Glendinning, gave me to understand that I had effected
his total ruin under circumstances which, rendering him an object for the
pity of all, should have protected him from the ill offices even of a fiend.

What now might have been my conduct it is difficult to say. The pitiable
condition of my dupe had thrown an air of embarrassed gloom over all;
and, for some moments, a profound silence was maintained, during which
I could not help feeling my cheeks tingle with the many burning glances of
scorn or reproach cast upon me by the less abandoned of the party. I will
even own that an intolerable weight of anxiety was for a brief instant lifted
from my bosom by the sudden and extraordinary interruption which ensued.
The wide, heavy folding doors of the apartment were all at once thrown

---

[5] Card game.

open, to their full extent, with a vigorous and rushing impetuosity that extinguished, as if by magic, every candle in the room. Their light in dying, enabled us just to perceive that a stranger had entered, about my own height, and closely muffled in a cloak. The darkness, however, was now total; and we could only *feel* that he was standing in our midst. Before any one of us could recover from the extreme astonishment into which this rudeness had thrown all, we heard the voice of the intruder.

"Gentlemen," he said, in a low, distinct, and never-to-be-forgotten *whisper* which thrilled to the very marrow of my bones, "Gentlemen, I make no apology for this behavior, because in thus behaving, I am but fulfilling a duty. You are, beyond doubt, uninformed of the true character of the person who has tonight won at *ecarte* a large sum of money from Lord Glendinning. I will therefore put you upon an expeditious and decisive plan of obtaining this very necessary information. Please to examine, at your leisure, the inner linings of the cuff of his left sleeve, and the several little packages which may be found in the somewhat capacious pockets of his embroidered morning wrapper."

While he spoke, so profound was the stillness that one might have heard a pin drop upon the floor. In ceasing, he departed at once, and as abruptly as he had entered. Can I—shall I describe my sensations? Must I say that I felt all the horrors of the damned? Most assuredly I had little time for reflection. Many hands roughly seized me upon the spot, and lights were immediately re-procured. A search ensued. In the lining of my sleeve were found all the court cards essential in *ecarte*, and, in the pockets of my wrapper, a number of packs, fac-similes of those used at our sittings, with the single exception that mine were of the species called, technically, *arrondees;* the honors being slightly convex at the ends, the lower cards slightly convex at the sides. In this disposition, the dupe who cuts, as customary, at the length of the pack, will invariably find that he cuts his antagonist an honor; while the gambler, cutting at the breadth, will, as certainly, cut nothing for his victim which may count in the records of the game.

Any burst of indignation upon this discovery would have affected me less than the silent contempt, or the sarcastic composure, with which it was received.

"Mr. Wilson," said our host, stooping to remove from beneath his feet an exceedingly luxurious cloak of rare furs, "Mr. Wilson, this is your property." (The weather was cold; and, upon quitting my own room, I had thrown a cloak over my dressing wrapper, putting it off upon reaching the scene of play.) "I presume it is supererogatory to seek here (eyeing the folds of the garment with a bitter smile) for any farther evidence of your skill. Indeed, we have had enough. You will see the necessity, I hope, of quitting Oxford—at all events, of quitting instantly my chambers."

Abased, humbled to the dust as I then was, it is probable that I should have resented this galling language by immediate personal violence, had not my whole attention been at the moment arrested by a fact of the most startling character. The cloak which I had worn was of a rare description of fur; how rare, how extravagantly costly, I shall not venture to say. Its fashion, too, was of my own fantastic invention; for I was fastidious to an absurd degree of coxcombry, in matters of this frivolous nature. When, therefore, Mr. Preston reached me that which he had picked up upon the floor, and near the folding-doors of the apartment, it was with an astonishment nearly bordering upon terror, that I perceived my own already hanging on my arm, (where I had no doubt unwittingly placed it,) and that the one presented me was but its exact counterpart in every, in even the minutest possible particular. The singular being who had so disastrously exposed me, had been muffled, I remembered, in a cloak; and none had been worn at all by any of the members of our party, with the exception of myself. Retaining some presence of mind, I took the one offered me by Preston; placed it, unnoticed, over my own; left the apartment with a resolute scowl of defiance; and, next morning ere dawn of day, commenced a hurried journey from Oxford to the continent, in a perfect agony of horror and of shame.

I fled in vain. My evil destiny pursued me as if in exultation, and proved, indeed, that the exercise of its mysterious dominion had as yet only begun. Scarcely had I set foot in Paris, ere I had fresh evidence of the detestable interest taken by this Wilson in my concerns. Years flew, while I experienced no relief. Villain!—at Rome, with how untimely, yet with how spectral an officiousness, stepped he in between me and my ambition! At Vienna, too—at Berlin—and at Moscow! Where in truth, had I *not* bitter cause to curse him within my heart? From his inscrutable tyranny did I at length flee, panic-stricken, as from a pestilence; and to the very ends of the earth *I fled in vain.*

And again, and again, in secret communion with my own spirit, would I demand the questions "Who is he?—whence came he?—and what are his objects?" But no answer was there found. And now I scrutinized, with a minute scrutiny, the forms, and the methods, and the leading traits of his impertinent supervision. But even here there was very little upon which to base a conjecture. It was noticeable, indeed, that, in no one of the multiplied instances in which he had of late crossed my path, had he so crossed it except to frustrate those schemes, or to disturb those actions, which, if fully carried out, might have resulted in bitter mischief. Poor justification this, in truth, for an authority so imperiously assumed! Poor indemnity for natural rights of self-agency so pertinaciously, so insultingly denied!

I had also been forced to notice that my tormentor, for a very long period of time, (while scrupulously and with miraculous dexterity maintaining his whim of an identity of apparel with myself,) had so contrived it, in the execution of his varied interference with my will, that I saw not, at any moment the features of his face. Be Wilson what he might, *this*, at least, was but the veriest of affectation, or of folly. Could he, for an instant, have supposed that, in my admonisher at Eton—in the destroyer of my honor at Oxford,—in him who thwarted my ambition at Rome, my revenge at Paris, my passionate love at Naples, or what he falsely termed my avarice in Egypt—that in this, my arch-enemy and evil genius, I could fail to recognise the William Wilson of my school-boy days,—the namesake, the companion, the rival,—the hated and dreaded rival at Dr. Bransby's? Impossible!—But let me hasten to the last eventful scene of the drama.

Thus far I had succumbed supinely to this imperious domination. The sentiment of deep awe with which I habitually regarded the elevated character, the majestic wisdom, the apparent omnipresence and omnipotence of Wilson, added to a feeling of even terror, with which certain other traits in his nature and assumptions inspired me, had operated, hitherto, to impress me with an idea of my own other weakness and helplessness, and to suggest an implicit, although bitterly reluctant submission to his arbitrary will. But, of late days, I had given myself up entirely to wine; and its maddening influence upon my hereditary temper rendered me more and more impatient of control, I began to murmur,—to hesitate,—to resist. And was it only fancy which induced me to believe that, with the increase of my own firmness, that of my tormentor underwent a proportional diminution? Be this as it may, I now began to feel the inspiration of a burning hope, and at length nurtured in my secret thoughts a stern and desperate resolution that I would submit no longer to be enslaved.

It was at Rome, during the Carnival of 18—, that I attended a masquerade in the palazzo of the Neapolitan Duke Di Broglio. I had indulged more freely than usual in the excesses of the wine-table; and now the suffocating atmosphere of the crowded rooms irritated me beyond endurance. The difficulty, too, of forcing my way through the mazes of the company contributed not a little to the ruffling of my temper; for I was anxiously seeking (let me not say with what unworthy motive) the young, the gay, the beautiful wife of the aged and doting Di Broglio. With a too unscrupulous confidence she had previously communicated to me the secret of the costume in which she would be habited, and now, having caught a glimpse of her person, I was hurrying to make my way into her presence. At this moment I felt a light hand placed upon my shoulder, and that ever-remembered, low, damnable *whisper* within my ear.

In an absolute frenzy of wrath, I turned at once upon him who had thus interrupted me, and seized him violently by the collar. He was attired, as I had expected, in a costume altogether similar to my own; wearing a Spanish cloak of blue velvet, begirt about the waist with a crimson belt sustaining a rapier. A mask of black silk entirely covered his face.

"Scoundrel!" I said, in a voice husky with rage, while every syllable I uttered seemed as new fuel to my fury; "scoundrel! impostor! accursed villain! you shall not—you *shall not* dog me unto death! Follow me, or I stab you where you stand!"—and I broke my way from the ball-room into a small antechamber adjoining, dragging him unresistingly with me as I went.

Upon entering, I thrust him furiously from me. He staggered against the wall, while I closed the door with an oath, and commanded him to draw. He hesitated but for an instant; then, with a slight sigh, drew in silence, and put himself upon his defence.

The contest was brief indeed. I was frantic with every species of wild excitement, and felt within my single arm the energy and power of a multitude. In a few seconds I forced him by sheer strength against the wainscoting, and thus, getting him at mercy, plunged my sword, with brute ferocity, repeatedly through and through his bosom.

At that instant some person tried the latch of the door. I hastened to prevent an intrusion, and then immediately returned to my dying antagonist. But what human language can adequately portray *that* astonishment, *that* horror which possessed me at the spectacle then presented to view? The brief moment in which I averted my eyes had been sufficient to produce, apparently, a material change in the arrangements at the upper or farther end of the room. A large mirror,—so at first it seemed to me in my confusion —now stood where none had been perceptible before; and, as I stepped up to it in extremity of terror, mine own image, but with features all pale and dabbed in blood, advanced to meet me with a feeble and tottering gait.

Thus it appeared, I say, but was not. It was my antagonist—it was Wilson, who then stood before me in the agonies of his dissolution. His mask and cloak lay, where he had thrown them, upon the floor. Not a thread in all his raiment—not a line in all the marked and singular lineaments of his face which was not, even in the most absolute identity, *mine own.*

It was Wilson; but he spoke no longer in a whisper, and I could have fancied that I myself was speaking while he said:

"*You have conquered, and I yield. Yet henceforward art thou also dead—dead to the World, to Heaven and to Hope! In me didst thou exist —and, in my death, see by this image, which is thine own, how utterly thou hast murdered thyself.*"

Questions for Discussion

1. Refer to the characteristics of romance mentioned in the Introduction and explain to what extent "William Wilson" is a romance and to what extent it is not.

2. How does the narrator's description of the school and his childhood prepare for the introduction of the double into the story?

3. To what extent are the narrator and the double alike and how do they differ? What do these differences and similarities tell you about the psychological state of the narrator?

4. Is "fatality" at all to blame for the narrator's fall from virtue?

5. What does the mirror symbolize at the end of the story?

6. Compare the use of the mirror as a symbol in this story and in "The Lady of Shalott."

Gustave Flaubert (1821–1880)

The Legend of St. Julian the Hospitaller

TRANSLATED BY F. W. DUPEE

I

Julian's father and mother lived in a castle on a hillside in the deep woods. At the four corners were pointed towers roofed with lead; the walls sprang from shafts of living rock which sloped steeply to the moat's bottom. The flagstones in the courtyard were tidy as a church floor; long spouts, representing dragons with their jaws wide, spat rainwater into cisterns; and at every window on every floor bloomed basil or heliotrope in painted pots.

Outside the castle was a second enclosure fenced in with stakes and containing first an orchard, then a flower garden of intricately patterned beds, then an arbor with many bowers where you sat to take the air, finally a playing field for the sport-loving pages. At the far side of the castle were kennels, stables and barns, a bakehouse and a winepress. Beyond lay green-turfed pastures, enclosed in turn by a stout hedge of thorn.

The castle had long been at peace with the world and the portcullis was never lowered now, grass grew in the moat, and swallows nested in the rotting battlements. If there was too much sun the bowman who paced the rampart all day long would retire into his sentry-house and sleep like a monk.

There was a gleam of polished metals in the great rooms; walls were hung with tapestries against the cold; cupboards bulged with linen, cellars with wine casks, coffers with bags of gold and silver coin. In the armory, among captive banners and the heads of hunted beasts, were weapons of every age and nation, from slings of the Amalekites and javelins of the

"The Legend of Saint Julian the Hospitaller" by Gustave Flaubert, translated by F. W. Dupee for *Great French Short Novels*. Reprinted by permission of F. W. Dupee.

Garamantes, to Saracen swords and Norman coats of mail. The great spit in the kitchen could roast an ox whole, the chapel was as splendid as a king's oratory. In a secluded corner there was even a Roman bath, although the old lord thought it a heathen device and abstained from putting it to use.

Wrapped always in a foxskin cape, he wandered about the castle, administering justice to his vassals and settling disputes among his neighbors. In winter he studied the flying snowflakes or had stories read to him. With the first fine days he rode out on his mule along country roads through fields of greening wheat, stopping every now and then to chat with the serfs and give them advice. He had many light loves, then at last took to wife a woman of the highest birth.

Pale, serious, a little proud, she wore headdresses which brushed the tops of doors and her train trailed three paces behind her. She ran her household as if it were a convent. Every morning she set the servants to their tasks, supervised the making of unguents and preserves, then turned to spinning or to embroidering altar cloths. She prayed God for a son and a son was born to her.

There was great rejoicing then. There was a feast that went on for three days and four nights while torches flared and harps sounded and the strewn greens wilted underfoot. Rare spices were eaten and fowls the size of sheep, and a dwarf entertained by emerging unexpectedly from a pie. The crowd swelled so from hour to hour that the supply of wine cups gave out at last and men took to swilling from helmets and hunting horns.

The young mother shunned the festivities, keeping quietly to her bed. One night she came suddenly awake and made out a sort of shadow in vague motion beneath her moon-streaked window. It was an old man in monk's cloth; he had a rosary at his side and a sack on his shoulder and the look and bearing of a hermit. He came toward her where she lay, and while his lips did not move, a voice spoke distinctly through them. "Be glad," it said, "be glad, O mother, for this son of yours will be a saint."

She would have cried out, but the old man rose softly into the air and glided off and out of sight along a streak of moonlight. Now the banqueters' voices grew loud in song. She heard angels' voices; and her head fell back upon the pillow, above which hung some great martyr's bone in a jeweled frame.

Next morning she questioned the servants, who denied having seen any hermit. What she herself had seen and heard then was surely a message from heaven whether it had happened in reality or in a dream. But she was careful not to speak of it for fear she should be accused of presumption.

The guests went off at daybreak and Julian's father had just seen the last of them out and was standing by the gate alone when someone emerged suddenly from the morning mist—a man with the braided beard and silver finery and intense dark stare of a gypsy. He began to speak, to stammer crazily, as if he were possessed. "Your son, your son!" he cried, and went on to speak of someone "winning a lot of glory and shedding a lot of blood," and he ended by hailing Julian's parents as "the blest family of an emperor." The excited lord tossed him a purse full of coins. The man stooped to retrieve it, the high grass covered him, and he was gone. Looking this way and that the old lord called and called again. No answer! The wind was loud, the mists of morning blew away.

He blamed the vision on his exhausted state: he had been too long without sleep. "I shall be laughed at if I speak of it," he thought but the glory promised to his son continued to excite him even though he was unsure that he had heard the prophecy aright or that he had heard anything at all.

Husband and wife kept their secrets from each other but loved their son equally and made much of him and were intensely careful of his person because they believed him to be chosen by God. He lay in his down-stuffed cradle, a dove-shaped lamp burning always just above; three nurses kept the cradle in motion; and with his blue eyes and rosy cheeks, his heavy swaddling, his embroidered gown and pearl-sewn cap, he did really resemble an infant Jesus. He cut all his teeth without crying.

When he was seven his mother taught him to sing and his father put him astride a huge battle horse to make him brave. The boy smiled with pleasure and soon was expert in the lore of battle horses. Meanwhile a learned old monk taught him Holy Writ, the Arabic numerals, the Latin alphabet and how to make dainty pictures on vellum. They worked together in a tower room high above the uproar of the castle; and when the lesson was over they came down into the garden to stroll and pause, studying the flowers.

Sometimes a train of pack animals was seen advancing through the valley below, driven by a man dressed like an Oriental. The lord, knowing the driver for a merchant, would send a servant after him: and the driver, confident of not being robbed, would consent to turn out of his road and be conducted into the great hall where he would throw open his trunks and hand around the many treasures within: the silks and velvets and perfumes and jewels, the various curios and inventions whose use was unknown in those parts. Finally he would be off, greatly enriched and quite unharmed. Or some pilgrim band would come knocking at the gate and when they had been fed and their wet clothes hung steamingly by the fire they would recount the story of their travels: the errant rocking voyages by sea, the long marches over hot sands, the fury of the paynims, the Syrian caves, the Manger and the Sepulcher. Before leaving they would present the young lords with seashells such as they wore sewed to their coats in token of their travels.

There were days when the lord feasted his old companions-at-arms. They drank and talked, recalling old engagements: the fortresses stormed, the rams and catapults making their din, the terrible wounds. Julian shouted as he listened and his father was now convinced that some day he would be a conqueror. But then evening came, and seeing the noble modesty with which, after prayers, he went among the kneeling poor to distribute alms, his mother decided that he was a future archbishop.

His place in chapel was next to his parents and even when the services were very protracted he stayed quietly on his knees with hands clasped firmly and his cap beside him on the floor. One day during Mass he looked up and saw a small white mouse creep from a hole in the wall, travel the length of the first altar step, explore about uncertainly, then trot back to its hole. Thinking to see the mouse again next Sunday, he felt strangely anxious. He did see it: the mouse reappeared; and each Sunday thereafter he watched for it, more and more anxious, hating the creature, intent on destroying it. So one Sunday after Mass he closed the door and strewed crumbs along the altar steps and stood waiting by the hole, armed with a stick. Long minutes passed, a small pink snout appeared, at last the entire mouse. He struck lightly, then stood amazed when the small body no longer moved. On the floor was a single drop of blood. Hastily Julian wiped it up with his sleeve, and tossed the dead mouse outside, saying nothing to anyone.

So many small birds pecked at the seeds in the garden that he thought of making a weapon out of a hollow reed filled with dried peas. When he came upon some tree that was noisy with birds, he approached it quietly, leveled his shooter, and blew out his cheeks. Birds came raining down in such abundance that he laughed aloud, pleased with his cleverness. As he was returning one morning along the rampart he spied a fat pigeon taking the sun there. He stopped to look at it; and as the wall was breached at this point and loose stones lay at hand, he grabbed one and swung and the bird dropped heavily into the moat.

He raced down after it, tearing his flesh on the brambles, searching wildly, as keen on the hunt as a young dog. The pigeon hung quivering in a bush with its wing broken. Its obstinate life filled him with rage. He took its throat in his hands and squeezed; the bird's struggles made his heart pound and his loins crawl with a strange lust and when it finally stiffened he was close to fainting.

At supper that night his father announced that the boy was old enough to learn to hunt. He got out an ancient book treating of the art of venery, written in the form of questions and answers exchanged between some master hunter and a pupil. It told how to train dogs and falcons, set traps, know a stag by its droppings, a fox by its tracks, a wolf by its lair, how best to start and track animals, where they are apt to take cover, which winds are most favorable, what cries to employ in the chase and what rules govern the division of the quarry. When Julian was able to repeat all this by heart his father made him a present of a magnificent pack of hunting dogs. There were twenty-four Barbary greyhounds, faster than gazelles but terribly wild and apt to get out of hand. There were seventeen pairs of loud-baying deep-chested white-and-russet Breton dogs, which looked wild but were easily controlled. For hunting wild boar with their ugly tactic of doubling back on the hunter, there were forty great shaggy boarhounds; and for bison hunting there were Tartary mastiffs which stood almost as tall as a jackass. Spaniels' black coats shone like satin: the beagles sang out and setters yapped in chorus. In a yard by themselves were eight growling, eye-rolling, chain-rattling bulldogs—terrible beasts that leap at men's throats and are quite unafraid of lions.

Every dog in the pack ate white bread, drank from troughs of hewn stone, and answered to some high-sounding name.

At that the dogs were probably inferior to the falcons. Spending money freely, the old lord acquired tiercelets from the Caucasus, sakers from Babylonia, gerfalcons from Germany; he had the kind of pilgrim-hawks which are only captured along the high shores of cold seas in far parts of the world. A special shed housed all the birds; there they were chained along a perch according to size, and let out every so often to stretch and play on their own strip of turf. In the shops of the castle men were busy making purse-nets, hooks, traps and snares of all kinds.

Julian's family sometimes got up large parties to go quail hunting in the fields. There the bird dogs soon began to point, then crouched motionless while the runners-in advanced with care and spread an immense net over and around them. A word from the huntsmen and the dogs barked, the quail took wing, and the ladies of the neighborhood with their husbands, children and maidservants, dashed for the net and captured the birds with ease. Or hares were started by beating on drums or foxes tumbled into pits or wolves thrust unsuspecting paws into cruel traps.

But Julian scorned these easy contrivances, preferring to hunt alone with horse and hawk. The hawk was usually a great white Scythian tararet, which perched firmly on his master's arm while they covered the plain at a gallop, a plume nodding on its leather hood and golden bells tinkling around its blue claws. When Julian loosed the jesses, letting him go, the wonderful bird shot arrow-like into the sky. Julian saw two specks circle and meet and vanish into the blue altitudes; then the falcon would drop dizzily from the skies, tearing at some bird in his claws, and resume his perch on the gauntlet with shaking wings. So Julian hunted heron, kites, crows and vultures.

He loved also to sound his horn and follow the dogs as they raced down the hills and jumped the streams and climbed to the next woods; and when a stag fell among them, moaning as they attacked it with their teeth, he skillfully dispatched it, then looked on with pleasure while they tore and devoured the bloody carcass.

On foggy days he hid out in the marshes to watch for geese, otter or wild duck. Three of his squires would have been waiting for him on the steps since daybreak; and even though the old monk his teacher made admonitory signs at him from his high window, Julian refused to look back. He went out in rain or storm or broiling sun, drank with his cupped hand from springs, ate wild apples, snatched brief naps under trees; and reached home at midnight with burrs in his hair, mud and gore on his clothes, and the smell of game all over him. Gradually he came to resemble the wild things he hunted. He was indifferent to his mother's entreaties, cold to her kisses, and seemed to be caught in the dark toils of a dream.

He killed bears with a knife, bulls with a hatchet and wild boars with a spear. And once, with nothing but a stick, he kept off a lot of wolves which were feeding on the corpses around a gallows.

There came a winter morning when he set out before daybreak, thoroughly equipped, with his bow astride his shoulder and his quiver slung to his pommel. A couple of terriers trailed his Danish hunter, all three of them keeping step and pounding the ground in unison while the wind blew and frost collected on his coat. Toward the east the sky began to clear and in the pallid light he saw a multitude of rabbits leaping and running among their burrows. Immediately the dogs were among them, upon them, cracking their frail spines. Next he was in a stretch of woods and, spying a woodcock that perched as if frozen to a branch, with head under wing, he made at it with a backstroke of his sword and severed its two feet from its body and was off without stopping to retrieve it.

Three hours more and he was cresting a mountain so immensely high that the heavens hung blue-black around him; and there in front of him was an expanse of flat rock with a precipice beyond and a couple of wild goats standing far out on it gazing idly into the gulf. Having no arrows—he had left his horse behind—he decided to fall directly upon them; and so, barefoot, bent double, dagger in hand, he advanced painfully towards them and brought the near one down with a sudden thrust in the ribs. The other, in a panic, leaped towards the void and Julian was after it to strike it down in turn when he stumbled and fell headlong across the body of the dead goat and there he lay, arms flung wide, staring down into space.

Then he was on the flats once more, following a willow-bordered stream, and a great number of cranes were in low shuttling flight above his head. Julian cut them all down, one by one, with his whip.

Meanwhile, the day grew warmer, the frost melted and the sun broke through the haze. He now saw far off, lead-gray and gleaming, a small lake, and breasting its bright still surface was some unknown beaver-like animal.

Across the distance he let fly an arrow and saw the creature sink and was sorry because he could not bring home the skin.

Now he was in an avenue of great trees, and passing under them as under some triumphal arch he entered a forest that lay beyond. A deer suddenly broke cover there, a buck showed in a side road, a badger came out of a hole, a peacock spread his tail along the grass; and when he had slain them all, there suddenly was another deer, more bucks and badgers sprang up around him, more peacocks and jays and blackbirds and foxes and porcupines and polecats and lynxes—an infinity of beasts, increasing as he advanced.

They crowded round him, trembling, with eyes of mild entreaty. But Julian attacked them tirelessly, having no thought except to be upon them with arrow or sword or knife. There was only the brute fact of his existence to remind him that he had been hunting for incalculable hours in some vague country where things happened with the same ease as in our dreams.

Then he saw an astonishing thing that made him pause at last. There opened before him a steep-sided sandy-bottomed valley, a sort of natural coliseum; and it was full of stags, an army of them, which huddled close and breathed warmth on one another, the steamy cloud from a hundred nostrils rising to mingle with the morning haze. For a moment, the prospect of so much slaughter made Julian go faint with excitement; then, springing from his horse, he thrust back his sleeves and began to take aim. With the twang of the first arrow all the stags looked up as one, a diffused moan broke from them, fissures opened in their solid ranks and panic shook the whole herd. As Julian's arrows fell upon them, hemmed in as they were by the valley walls, the herd stampeded. Stags reared, pawed, locked antlers, climbed heavily on each other. And all the while they fell, bodies and antlers piling up into one vast inextricable ever-growing ever-shifting mound. So one by one, with heavy lungs and bursting bowels, they died along the sands and soon everything was still and night came down and the tree-screened sky was the color of blood.

Julian leaned against a tree and stared on the enormous massacre, trying to remember how it had been done. Then across the valley at the wood's edge he saw another stag with its hind and fawn. Dark, enormous, the stag had a white beard and an intricate many-pointed growth of horn; the hind, pale as a dead leaf, grazed idly by while her spotted fawn trotted alongside, pulling at her dugs. Again Julian's bow sang out. The fawn dropped. The mother, looking up, uttered a single shattering all but human cry. Julian, tense, exasperated, brought her down as well, with a shot full in the breast. Seeing her fall the great stag leaped and received Julian's arrow, his last one, between the eyes. There it stuck fast but the stag, indifferent, came striding over the bodies of his dead, came on and on, while Julian retreated in horror, seeing himself charged and laid flat and disemboweled. Then the

great stag halted and with burning eyes, solemn, accusing, like some patri-
arch or judge, he spoke, while off in the distance a bell tolled.

"Accurst! accurst! accurst! one day, O savage heart, you will destroy
your father and mother."

The stag dropped quietly to earth and closed his eyes and died.

Julian stood as if stunned; then a weariness swept over him, followed by
great waves of disgust and sadness. His horse was lost, his dogs had taken
to their heels, the solitude around him seemed full of vague alarms. He fled,
striking across country, following a trail at random. And there, suddenly,
was the castle gate.

That night he did not sleep but lay staring into the uneven light of the
hanging lamp and saw always the great black, bearded wide-antlered stag.
The stag's words obsessed him; repeatedly he denied them. "It cannot be
that I shall kill them. No, no! I have no wish to kill them." Then in a moment
he thought, "But suppose I *should* wish—" And he lay and trembled for
fear the Devil should implant that unspeakable wish in him.

Three months his mother prayed in anguish by his bed while his father,
groaning, paced the corridors. Specialists were brought in, famous doctors
and apothecaries; they said he was sick with a miasma or with carnal desire; they prescribed drugs and more drugs. When they questioned him,
however, Julian merely shook his head.

Growing stronger, he walked briefly in the courtyard, leaning on his
father and the old monk. When he had quite recovered he obstinately refused
to hunt again. His father, hoping to bring him around, made him a present
of a fine stout Saracen sword. It hung aloft on a pillar among other arms
and trophies, and Julian had to mount a ladder to bring it down. It was
very heavy and slipped from his hands, and clattering down, grazed the old
lord's shoulder and slashed his mantle. Julian fainted, thinking he had killed
his father.

From then on he felt a horror of weapons and went white at the sight of
a bare blade. This weakness grieved his family and at last the old monk, in
the name of God, honor, and the ancestral dead, bade him take up again the
exercises of a gentleman.

The squires amused themselves by practicing daily with javelins. Julian
soon excelled at this sport and could drive his javelin into a bottle's mouth
or strike the tail-feathers from a weathercock or pick out doornails at a hundred paces.

One summer evening he loitered in the arbor, now dim in the falling
light; and spying around the arbor, against a wall, what he thought to be two
white fluttering wings, surely a stork, he hurled his javelin. There was a
terrible cry; it was the voice of his mother, whose bonnet with its long white
fluttering ribbons stayed pinned to the wall.

Julian fled the castle and was seen there no more.

II

He fell in with a passing troop of adventuring soldiers and came to know thirst, hunger, fever, and vermin, the noise of battle, the sight of dying men. His skin browned in the wind; his arms and legs grew hard under the weight of his armor; and being strong, fearless, just and shrewd, he was soon in command of a company.

With sword aloft he waved his men into battle; he scaled fortress walls by night, hanging to knotted ropes, tugged at by the wind, while sparks of Greek fire clung to his cuirass and boiling tar and molten lead poured hissing down from the battlements. Stones crashed on his buckler, shivering it; bridges overloaded with men gave way beneath him. On one occasion he felled fourteen men with a single swing of his battle-ax; in the lists he overcame all challengers; many times he was left on the field for dead.

Yet he always walked away, thanks to the divine favor which he enjoyed now, because he had become the protector of churchmen, orphans, widows and aged men. Of aged men most of all, and seeing some old stranger on the road ahead he would call out to him to show his face, as if afraid he might kill him in error.

Desperate men flocked to his banner, runaway slaves, serfs in revolt, bastards without fortune; and soon he had an army of his own, its fame increasing with its numbers, until the world sought him out and he was able to give aid by turns to the French Dauphin, the English king, the Templars of Jerusalem, the Surena of the Parthians, the Negus of Abyssinia, the Emperor of Calcutta. He did battle with Scandinavians in fish-scale armor, with Negroes astride red asses and brandishing shields of hippopotamus hide, with East Indians the color of pale gold who waved shining swords and wore their crowns into battle. He subdued the Troglodytes and the Anthropophages. He journeyed through hot countries where men's hair took fire from the sun and they flared up like torches, through cold countries where men's arms snapped freezing from their sockets and fell heavily to earth, through fog-bound countries where they marched among phantoms.

He was consulted by republics in distress, he conferred with ambassadors and obtained unexpected terms, he rebuked tyrants, delivered captive queens and set whole peoples free. It was Julian and no other who slew the Milanese serpent and the dragon of Oberbirbach.

Now the Emperor of Occitania was victorious over the Spanish Moslems and took the Caliph of Cordova's sister as his concubine and by her had a daughter whom he brought up in the Christian faith. But the Caliph, feigning a desire to be converted, arrived with a numerous escort as if on a visit to the Emperor, put his entire garrison to the sword and threw him into a dungeon where he used him cruelly to extort his treasure.

Julian hastened to his aid, destroyed the infidel army, laid siege to the town, slew the Caliph, chopped off his head and tossed it over the ramparts like a ball. Then he released the Emperor and set him on his throne again in the presence of his entire court. By way of rewards the Emperor offered him money, whole basketfuls; Julian would have none of it. Did he want more?—the Emperor offered him three-quarters of his wealth and was refused again; then half his kingdom; Julian thanked him and declined. The Emperor was in tears, he saw no way of showing his gratitude. At last he slapped his brow and turned whispering to one of his attendants; a curtain was drawn and there stood a young girl.

Her great dark eyes were like two soft lights and she had a charming smile. Her curls tangled with the jewels on her half-open bodice; through her transparent tunic shone the young lines of her body, which was plump, small, finely made.

Julian was dazzled, all the more because he had been chaste till now. So he took the Emperor's daughter in marriage, with a castle which she held from her mother and, the wedding over, quitted his host after an exchange of many courtesies.

Their palace was built of white marble in the Moorish style and stood on a promontory among orange groves. There was an expanse of bright bay below, a fanlike spread of forest behind, and terraces of flowers descending to a rosy beach where small shells crackled underfoot. The sky was an unchanging blue. Trees stirred in light winds that blew, now from off the sea, now down from the steep all-enveloping mountains.

The rooms were full of shadow yet drew soft light from encrusted walls. Tall reedlike columns supported domed vaults sculptured to represent stalactites in a cave. In the great halls were fountains, in the courts mosaics, on the walls festoons; delicate instances of architectural fancy abounded; and such was the silence everywhere that you could hear plainly the rustle of a scarf, the echo of a sigh.

Julian made war no longer but lived at ease among a tranquil people, contingents of them arriving daily to kneel before him and kiss his hand and do him homage like people of the East, while he lounged in purple dress in some deep-set window and called to mind the old hunting days. He longed to hunt again, to scour the desert after gazelle and ostrich, stalk leopards among the bamboos, strike into forests full of rhinoceros, scale impossible mountains where the eagle screamed, and wrestle with bears on icebergs in the polar sea. Sometimes, in dreams, he saw himself like our father Adam sitting in the middle of Paradise with the entire race of animals around him. He stretched forth an arm and they died. Or else they paraded before him two by two in order of size, from elephants and lions to ermines and ducks, as on the day when they entered Noah's ark. Standing in a cave's mouth, hidden, he rained darts on them, darts that never missed. More animals appeared, endless animals, until, wild-eyed, he woke at last.

There were princes among his acquaintance who invited him to hunt. He refused, thinking by such penance to turn aside the curse. He believed that the fate of his father and mother was linked in some way with the slaughtering of animals. Yet he grieved because he could not see his parents; and his other great desire, the secret one, became more and more unbearable.

His wife hoped to divert him and so engaged jugglers and dancers to perform in the castle, or traveled with him into the country in an open litter, or lay beside him in a boat while they watched the play of wandering fish in sky-clear water. She pelted him with flowers; she sat at his feet and plucked charmingly at the three strings of an old mandolin; and then, in despair, "My dear good lord, what ails you?" she asked mildly, laying a hand on his shoulder.

For a long time he refused to answer though sometimes he wept. Then one day he told her what was horribly on his mind. She fought against it, she argued well. Very probably his father and mother were dead already; and if by chance they were alive still and he should see them again, whatever could make him commit so abominable an act, what weird circumstance or impossible motive? His fears were all groundless, she said, and he should go back to hunting. Julian listened smiling but could not bring himself to yield.

One August night as they were preparing for sleep and she was already in bed and Julian was at his prayers, he heard a fox barking at a distance and, nearer by, directly under the window, soft, stealthy, padding footfalls. Now he was at the window and looking down in the gloom on some vague prowling forms, the shadows, as it were, of animals. He was too strongly tempted. From its hook on the wall, he seized his old quiver; and when his wife looked at him, astonished, he said, "You see! I obey you. I shall be back at sunrise." Suddenly she was afraid and began to speak of accidents and injuries but Julian comforted her and left, surprised to see her so changed.

Soon afterwards a page informed her that two strangers had come inquiring for her lord; in his absence they begged to see his lady at once. They came in to her, an aged couple, each of them leaning heavily on a stick, the dust of the road on their ragged clothes. They made bold to say that they brought news of Julian's father and mother and she leaned from her bed to listen. But first they exchanged a glance and asked if he ever spoke of his parents, still loved them.

"Ah, yes!" she said.

"Well, we are his parents!" they cried, and sat themselves down because they were very tired.

She hesitated. Could it be so? They guessed her doubt and went on to offer proof by describing a curious birthmark on Julian's body. She leaped from bed crying to the page to bring them food. But hungry as they looked, they ate little and she saw how their bony fingers shook when they raised their cups. She answered their many questions about their son but took pains to conceal his terrible obsession. They told her that they had left their castle when Julian failed to return, and wandered for years in search of him, following vague clues, never losing hope. So much of their money had gone into meeting river tolls and inn charges, princes' exactions and those of highwaymen, that they were now quite penniless and had to beg their way. But what of that, when they would soon be able to take Julian in their arms! How happy he must be to have so pretty a wife, they said; and they gazed long at her and kissed her and kissed her. The fine room made them stare; and the old man inquired why the walls bore the Emperor of Occitania's coat-of-arms.

"He is my father," she said.

He started, remembering what the gypsy had prophesied, while his wife called to mind the prophecy of the hermit. No doubt their son's present happiness promised some even greater, some eternal, glory to come; and the old couple sat wide-eyed in the blaze of the great candelabra on the table.

They must have been very handsome in their youth. The mother, her fine abundant hair intact, wore it in lengthy white braids along her cheek; while the father, with his great height and great beard, resembled some statue in a church. Julian's wife persuaded them not to wait up for him. She made them sleep in her own bed, tucked them away like children and drew the curtains. They were asleep soon, and outside, in the first gleams of dawn, small birds were singing.

Julian had crossed the park and come into the forest, his step eager, his senses alert to the soft grass and mild moonlit air. Shadows were deep on the moss banks under trees. At intervals there were moon-drenched clearings where he abruptly halted, thinking he was about to plunge into a woodland pond; and there were real ponds, which he mistook for clearings. Everywhere the silence was intense; there was no trace of the animals which only a moment ago had been prowling around the castle. He was now in a dense stand of trees where the gloom was especially thick. He felt the play of warm scented airs on his flesh. His feet sank among dead leaves and he stopped, leaning breathless against an oak.

Then a dark, still darker, something leaped suddenly from behind him, a wild boar, which was off before he had time to seize his bow and which he mourned the loss of as if that was a great misfortune. Leaving the woods he spied a wolf stealing along a hedge and let fly an arrow. The wolf stopped, looked briefly around at him, and went on. It trotted evenly along, keeping the same distance from him, halting at intervals; but when Julian started to take aim, it fled. Thus he covered a wide plain, then a tract of sand hills, and came out on high ground overlooking miles of country below.

He was among great flat jumbled stones, the scatterings of some old graveyard long abandoned to the weather. He stumbled over moldy crosses leaning sadly askew among the stones, and he trod on the bones of the dead. There was a stirring of vague shapes in the dark of the tombs, hyenas in wild-eyed panting flight. Their hooves came clattering over the stones and they closed in on Julian, sniffing, yawning, showing their gums. He drew his sword and they fled, severally, at a headlong limping gallop, kicking up a dust which finally hid them from sight.

Later, in a ravine, there was a wild bull pawing the sand and menacing him with lowered horns. Julian thrust at it with his lance but the lance sang out and fell in splinters as if it had come against some bull cast in bronze and he closed his eyes, expecting to be charged and killed. When he opened them the bull was gone.

His heart sank with shame, his strength gave way before some higher power, and striking back into the forest, he headed for home. He was in a tangle of creepers, cutting a passage with his sword, when a weasel shot between his legs; a panther, leaping, cleared his shoulder; around the trunk of an ash a snake coiled upward; from out the leaves above, a huge jackdaw eyed him; and it was as if the sky had rained down all its stars upon the forest, for everywhere around him, sparking the darkness, were the innumerable eyes of beasts—owls, squirrels, monkeys, parrots, bobcats.

Julian attacked them with arrows but the feathered shafts only showered like white butterflies among the leaves. He threw stones, but they dropped harmlessly to earth. He raged, cursed himself, made the forest loud with imprecations. Then the various animals he had just been hunting showed themselves and came round him in a narrow circle, keeping erect or going down on their haunches. There he stood in the midst of them, terrified and quite unable to move. By making a great effort he succeeded in taking a step forward. As soon as he moved, wings began to flutter in the trees, paws stirred on the ground, and the whole assemblage moved with him. He went on, the hyenas striding ahead, the wolf and the boar behind; the bull, swinging an enormous head, on his left; the snake coiling along through the grass on his right; the panther advancing at a distance with arched back and long soft-footed strides. He walked very slowly to avoid exciting them and as he went he saw porcupines, foxes, jackals, vipers and bears breaking cover around him. He began to run and they ran too. The snake hissed, the dirtier creatures slavered; he felt the boar's tusk prodding at his heels, the wolf's hairy snout nuzzling his hand. Monkeys pinched him and made faces; a weasel somersaulted over his feet; a bear knocked his cap from his head with a backswing of its paw; and the panther, after chewing placidly on an arrow, let it drop with disdain.

There was irony in their sly motions. Watching him from the corners of their eyes, they seemed to be planning some revenge; and Julian, dazed by buzzing insects and the slapping of birds' tails and the breath from many nostrils, walked like a blind man with eyes closed and arms flung out, not daring even to cry, "Have mercy!"

A cock crowed, others replied, day was breaking; and Julian made out the lines of the castle roof riding above the orange trees. Then he discovered some partridges fluttering in a stubblefield close by. He flung off his cloak and threw it over them like a net. On lifting it, however, he found only the decaying body of a bird long dead. This was the worst irony yet; he raged anew; the thirst to kill came over him and, failing beasts, he would gladly have killed men. Quickly he mounted the three terraces and with a blow of his fist swung the door wide. But on the stairs within he remembered his darling wife and his heart softened. She was no doubt asleep and he would have the pleasure of surprising her. Quietly, his sandals in his hand, he turned the knob and entered their bedroom.

The early light came dimly through leaded windows. Julian stumbled over some clothes lying on the floor; a little farther, and he knocked against a table loaded with dishes. "She must have eaten," he thought and advanced with caution towards the alcove where, in total darkness, the bed stood. He stooped to kiss his wife, bending over the two who lay there side by side in sleep. His lips touched a man's beard and he fell back, thinking he was out of his mind. He stooped over the bed again and this time his searching fingers discovered a woman's long hair. To assure himself that he had been mistaken, he felt for the beard again—and found it! found a man there, a man lying with his wife.

He was upon them in a fury, striking with his dagger, foaming, stamping, howling like a wild beast. At last he stopped. Pierced through the heart they had not so much as stirred, they were dead. He heard the rattle of death in their throats, rhythmic, prolonged, growing feebler at last, mingling then with another sound, now vague and far off, now coming steadily closer, swelling, ringing out cruelly; and he recognized in terror the belling of the great black stag.

He turned and saw in the door, candle in hand, ghostlike, the pale figure of his wife. Drawn there by the sounds of violence, she took it all in with one wide glance and fled in horror, dropping the candle. Julian picked it up.

His father and mother lay face up before him with great wounds in their breasts. In their superb gentle eyes was the look of people intent on keeping a secret forever. There was blood on their white hands, the bedclothes, the floor, the ivory crucifix on the alcove wall. The glare of the newly risen sun made the whole room red as if with blood. Julian looked at the dead. He said to himself, endeavored to believe, that this thing could not be, that he must be entangled in some fearful error. To make sure of their identity he stooped close over the old man's face and saw beneath open lids two eyes, now glazed, which scorched him like fire. He then circled the bed to where, in the dark recesses of the alcove, the other body lay, the face half hidden by white hair. He lifted the head with one hand and with the other held the candle close to it while drop by drop the bed discharged its load of blood upon the floor.

At evening he came in where his wife was and speaking with a stranger's voice bade her first of all not to answer him or come near him or even look at him; then to obey, under penalty of damnation, his various commands, every one of which she must consider irrevocable.

In the death-chamber she would find written instructions for the funeral. These she must carry out to the letter. To her he made over everything he owned: castle, serfs, goods—even the clothes on his back and the sandals on his feet, which she would find presently at the stair head.

The dead were splendidly interred in an abbey church at three days' journey from the castle. A monk, his face concealed by his hood, followed the procession at a distance and to him no one dared speak. All during the Mass he lay flat on the porch floor, his arms crossed, his face in the dust.

After the burial he was seen to take the road leading to the mountains. He looked back at intervals and finally was gone.

III

He went about the world begging his way. He reached up a hand to horsemen on the roads, bent a knee to reapers in the fields, stood patiently at castle gates, and looked so grief-stricken that he was not refused. Humbly, again and again, he told his story and people fled crossing themselves. When he passed through a village where he had been before, they abused and stoned him and shut their doors in his face, although a few charitable souls put plates of food on their windowsills before banging the shutters on the unholy sight of him.

Shunned by all, he began to shun mankind himself, feeding on roots, plants and windfalls, and shellfish gathered along the beaches of the world. Sometimes, on coming over a hill, he would find himself in sight of some multitudinous jumble of roofs and spires below; from the dark maze of streets came the steady hum of human life and he would be drawn downward by a need to be with other people. No sooner was he in the streets, however, than the brutal look on people's faces, the bustle in the stores, the uproar of shops and foundries, the callous idle talk, would begin to freeze his heart. On feast days when bells began tolling at daybreak and people responded with excitement, he watched them pouring from their houses, the dancers in the public squares, the beer fountains at the crossroads, the rich bright hangings on the princely houses; and then after dark he spied through windows on the long family tables where old people sat with children in their laps. He would turn away in tears and strike back into the country.

He gazed with yearning at colts in their pastures, birds in their nests, insects among flowers; all fled at his approach. He sought out deserted places but there was the rattle of death in the blowing of wind, tears in the dew-drops, blood in the sun at evening, and parricide by night in his dreams. He undertook acts of mortification, ascended on his knees to high and holy places. But the horror in his mind corrupted the splendor of tabernacles and nullified the rigor of his penances. He did not curse God for having caused him to murder, but having murdered he despaired of God. The horror he felt of his own person made him risk it eagerly in dangerous enterprises. He rescued children from pits in the earth and helpless men and women from their burning houses. But the earth rejected him, the flames spared him. With the passing of time he suffered not less but more and finally he resolved to die.

One day, however, while he was staring into a spring of water to judge of its depth, he saw appear on the far side an old man with so much misery on his lean white-bearded face that Julian suddenly wept. The old man fell to weeping too; and Julian, looking him in the face, knew him and did not know him. "My father!" he cried and thought no more of destroying himself.

So, weighed down with memories, he traversed many lands and came at last to a river which tore along swiftly between marshy shores and had long defied anyone to cross it. Mud-bound and half concealed in the reeds lay an old boat, and on looking around Julian also discovered a pair of oars. It came over him that he might devote his life to the service of others.

He began by constructing a sort of ramp across the marsh, connecting the river's channel with solid ground. He broke his nails on enormous stones, carried them pressed against his heaving stomach, sprawled in the mud, sank into it, was nearly drowned several times. Then he set to patching up the boat from the debris of other vessels and he made himself a hut of logs and clay.

Travelers soon heard of Julian's ferry and began to flock to it. On the far side a flag was raised to summon him and Julian would leap aboard and row across for the waiting passengers. The boat was heavy to begin with and when it was loaded with men and their belongings including domestic animals that kicked and reared in alarm, it could only be managed with difficulty. He asked nothing for his trouble though some of the passengers gave him wornout clothes or leftovers from their store of food. The ugly ones cursed him out and he reproved them gently. If they went on cursing, he was satisfied to bless them.

A small table, a stool, a bed made of dry leaves, and three earthen bowls were all the furnishings he had while a couple of holes in the wall served as windows. In front the great river rolled its turgid green flood; at the rear stretched a vast colorless barrens strewn with shallow ponds. In spring the damp soil reeked of decay; then came powerful winds driving dust before them till it roiled the water and gritted between his teeth; then came mosquitoes in endless humming biting clouds; then appalling frosts which turned the earth to stone and gave him in his chilled and exhausted state a tremendous appetite for meat. Months passed when Julian, seeing no one, sat with his eyes shut trying to revive in memory the days of his youth. A castle courtyard would rise before him with greyhounds at rest on the terraces, grooms busy in the armory, and a yellow-haired boy sitting in a bower of vines between an old man wrapped in furs and a lady in a tall bonnet. Suddenly an image of two dead bodies would intervene and he would fling himself on his bed and sob, "Ah, poor father! Poor mother, poor mother!" and, dozing off, he would continue to see them in dreams.

There came a night when he thought he heard someone calling him in his sleep. He strained to listen but made out nothing except the river's roar. Then "Julian!" the same voice cried again, "Julian!" It reached him, amazingly, from the far shore of the broad and noisy river. "Julian!" he heard again, the voice loud, vibrant, like a church bell. With lantern alight, he stepped from the hut into a night wild with wind and rain, the river foaming white in the intense darkness.

He hesitated briefly then leapt into the boat and cast off. Instantly the waves subsided and the boat sped easily to the far shore. There a man stood waiting in a ragged coat, his face white as a plaster mask, his eyes redder than coals. Holding up his lantern Julian saw that the stranger was covered with hideous sores. He was a leper but he had the majesty of a king. The boat gave alarmingly under his weight, then rose again, and Julian began to work the oars.

At every stroke the bow slapped against a wave and was flung aloft, while dark water streamed alongside. Masses of water gathered beneath, thrusting the boat skyward, then fell away, leaving it to skitter down into some deep trough where it spun helplessly. Julian could only keep it under control by leaning far forward and then, feet powerfully braced, hands riveted to the oar handles, flinging his torso backward with a convulsive pull at the oars. Hail cut his hands, rain poured down his back, and suddenly breathless in the terrible wind, he paused, letting the boat drift with the waves. But feeling that something very great was at stake, a mission that he must not fail, he once more seized the oars and made them rattle on their pins in the loud wind. At the bow the lantern burned, its rays intercepted at intervals by the fluttering passages of storm-blown birds. But always he saw the eyes of the Leper who stood immobile at the stern. And they were a long, long time in crossing.

Arrived in the hut Julian closed the door behind them. The Leper took the stool and sat. His shroudlike dress fell to his loins; his chest, his shoulders, his lean arms were plastered with sores. There were great pained wrinkles on his forehead. Skeleton-like, he had a hole instead of a nose; his lips were blue, a teamy and malodorous exhalation pouring from them.

"I am hungry!" he said.

Julian gave him what he had, a black loaf and rind of bacon. When he had devoured them, the table, bowl and knife handle bore the same sores that he had on his body. Then he said,

"I am thirsty!"

Julian went to get the water jug and found it full of some exciting sweet-smelling liquid. It was wine—a wonderful find. The Leper reached for it and drank the jug dry at a draught.

Then he said, "I am cold."

Julian put his candle to a heap of dried fern in the middle of the floor. The Leper, on his knees, crouched by the fire, body shaking, sores running, eyes growing dim. He was weakening visibly, and in a faint voice murmured,

"Your bed!"

Julian helped him to it gently and covered him with everything he had, even the tarpaulin for his boat. The Leper groaned through his teeth, the rattle of death came faster in his chest, and with every breath he took his belly sank into his spine. At last his eyes went closed.

"My bones are like ice! Come close to me!"

And Julian, raising the tarpaulin, lay down at his side on the dry leaves. The Leper turned his head. "Take off your clothes," he commanded, "that I may have the warmth of your body." Julian flung off his clothes and lay down once more as naked as on the day he was born. Against his thigh he felt the Leper's skin, colder than a snake and rough as a file. He tried to cheer him but the other merely said in a low whisper, "I am dying. Come closer, get me warm! No! not with your hands, with your whole body."

Julian laid himself at full length upon him, mouth to mouth, breast to breast. The Leper clasped him hard and suddenly his eyes shone like stars, the hair on his head was like the rays of the sun, his breath was like the breath of the rose, there was incense in the smoke of the fern-fire, music on the water. To Julian, fainting, came a great bliss, a joy more than human; and the one who held him grew tall, grew taller, till his head and feet touched the two walls of the hut. The roof gaped, the wide firmament looked down—

and Julian rose into blue altitudes face to face with Our Lord Jesus who carried him up to heaven.

And that is the story of Saint Julian the Hospitaller more or less as you will find it on a church window in my part of the country.

Questions for Discussion

1. Why is the future of Julian prophesied separately to his parents, and how is each prophesy appropriate to each parent to whom it is told?

2. Of what importance is the episode of the mouse?

3. Why does the author use so much detail in recounting his legend? Is such detail common to romances? How does it affect the legendary aspects of the tale?

4. Why is it stressed that Julian loves to hunt alone?

5. What significance do you attach to Julian's stumbling over the dead goat and lying on it?

6. What evidence is there that Julian is not quite real or human, particularly as a hunter? In this connection consider the stag episode.

7. What causes Julian to leave his parents' castle?

8. Why does Julian after his marriage associate his longing to see his parents with his desire to hunt again? What significance does this have? Is his killing of them inevitable?

9. What is meant by the author's remark that the animals Julian hunts just before the murder of his parents have "irony in their sly motions"?

10. Why is the Leper an appropriate instrument of Julian's penitence? Is his penitence at all similar to that of the Ancient Mariner?

Franz Kafka (1883–1924)

The Hunter Gracchus

TRANSLATED BY WILLA AND EDWIN MUIR

Two boys were sitting on the harbour wall playing with dice. A man was reading a newspaper on the steps of the monument, resting in the shadow of a hero who was flourishing his sword on high. A girl was filling her bucket at the fountain. A fruit-seller was lying beside his scales, staring out to sea. Through the vacant window and door openings of a café one could see two men quite at the back drinking their wine. The proprietor was sitting at a table in front and dozing. A bark was silently making for the little harbour, as if borne by invisible means over the water. A man in a blue blouse climbed ashore and drew the rope through a ring. Behind the boatman two other men in dark coats with silver buttons carried a bier, on which, beneath a great flower-patterned tasselled silk cloth, a man was apparently lying.

Nobody on the quay troubled about the newcomers; even when they lowered the bier to wait for the boatman, who was still occupied with his rope, nobody went nearer, nobody asked them a question, nobody accorded them an inquisitive glance.

The pilot was still further detained by a woman who, a child at her breast, now appeared with loosened hair on the deck of the boat. Then he advanced and indicated a yellowish two-storeyed house that rose abruptly on the left beside the sea; the bearers took up their burden and bore it to the low but gracefully pillared door. A little boy opened a window just in time to see the party vanishing into the house, then hastily shut the window again. The door too was now shut; it was of black oak, and very strongly made. A flock of doves which had been flying around the belfry alighted in the street before the house. As if their food were stored within, they assembled in front of the door. One of them flew up to the first storey and pecked at the window-pane. They were bright-hued, well-tended, beautiful birds. The woman on the boat flung grain to them in a wide sweep; they ate it up and flew across to the woman.

A man in a top hat tied with a band of crêpe now descended one of the narrow and very steep lanes that led to the harbour. He glanced round vigilantly, everything seemed to displease him, his mouth twisted at the sight of some offal in a corner. Fruit skins were lying on the steps of the monument; he swept them off in passing with his stick. He rapped at the house door, at the same time taking his top hat from his head with his black-gloved hand. The door was opened at once, and some fifty little boys appeared in two rows in the long entry-hall, and bowed to him.

The boatman descended the stairs, greeted the gentleman in black, conducted him up to the first storey, led him round the bright and elegant loggia which encircled the courtyard, and both of them entered, while the boys pressed after them at a respectful distance, a cool spacious room looking towards the back, from whose window no habitation, but only a bare, blackish grey rocky wall was to be seen. The bearers were busied in setting up and lighting several long candles at the head of the bier, yet these did not give light, but only scared away the shadows which had been immobile till then, and made them flicker over the walls. The cloth covering the bier had been thrown back. Lying on it was a man with wildly matted hair, who looked somewhat like a hunter. He lay without motion and, it seemed, without breathing, his eyes closed; yet only his trappings indicated that this man was probably dead.

The gentleman stepped up to the bier, laid his hand on the brow of the man lying upon it, then kneeled down and prayed. The boatman made a sign to the bearers to leave the room; they went out, drove away the boys who had gathered outside, and shut the door. But even that did not seem to satisfy the gentleman, he glanced at the boatman; the boatman understood, and vanished through a side door into the next room. At once the man on the bier opened his eyes, turned his face painfully towards the gentleman, and said: "Who are you?" Without any mark of surprise the gentleman rose from his kneeling posture and answered: "The Burgomaster of Riva."

The man on the bier nodded, indicated a chair with a feeble movement of his arm, and said, after the Burgomaster had accepted his invitation: "I knew that, of course, Burgomaster, but in the first moments of returning consciousness I always forget, everything goes round before my eyes, and it is best to ask about anything even if I know. You too probably know that I am the hunter Gracchus."

"Certainly," said the Burgomaster. "Your arrival was announced to me during the night. We had been asleep for a good while. Then towards midnight my wife cried: 'Salvatore'—that's my name—'look at that dove at the window.' It was really a dove, but as big as a cock. It flew over me and said in my ear: 'To-morrow the dead hunter Gracchus is coming; receive him in the name of the city.' "

The hunter nodded and licked his lips with the tip of his tongue: "Yes, the doves flew here before me. But do you believe, Burgomaster, that I shall remain in Riva?"

"I cannot say that yet," replied the Burgomaster. "Are you dead?"

"Yes," said the hunter, "as you see. Many years ago, yes, it must be a great many years ago, I fell from a precipice in the Black Forest— that is in Germany—when I was hunting a chamois. Since then I have been dead."

"But you are alive too," said the Burgomaster.

"In a certain sense," said the hunter, "in a certain sense I am alive too. My death ship lost its way; a wrong turn of the wheel, a moment's absence of mind on the pilot's part, a longing to turn aside towards my lovely native country, I cannot tell what it was; I only know this, that I remained on earth and that ever since my ship has sailed earthly waters. So I, who asked for nothing better than to live among my mountains, travel after my death through all the lands of the earth."

"And you have no part in the other world?" asked the Burgomaster, knitting his brow.

"I am for ever," replied the hunter, "on the great stair that leads up to it. On that infinitely wide and spacious stair I clamber about, sometimes up, sometimes down, sometimes on the right, sometimes on the left, always in motion. The hunter has been turned into a butterfly. Do not laugh."

"I am not laughing," said the Burgomaster in self-defence.

"That is very good of you," said the hunter. "I am always in motion. But when I make a supreme flight and see the gate actually shining before me I awaken presently on my old ship, still stranded forlornly in some earthly sea or other. The fundamental error of my one-time death grins at me as I lie in my cabin. Julia, the wife of the pilot, knocks at the door and brings me on my bier the morning drink of the land whose coasts we chance to be passing. I lie on a wooden pallet, I wear—it cannot be a pleasure to look at me— a filthy winding sheet, my hair and beard, black tinged with grey, have grown together inextricably, my limbs are covered with a great flower-patterned woman's shawl with long fringes. A sacramental candle stands at my head and lights me. On the wall opposite me is a little picture, evidently of a Bushman who is aiming his spear at me and taking cover as best he can behind a beautifully painted shield. On shipboard one is often a prey to stupid imaginations, but that is the stupidest of them all. Otherwise my wooden case is quite empty. Through a hole in the side wall come in the warm airs of the southern night, and I hear the water slapping against the old boat.

"I have lain here ever since the time when, as the hunter Gracchus living in the Black Forest, I followed a chamois and fell from a precipice. Everything happened in good order. I pursued, I fell, bled to death in a ravine, died, and this ship should have conveyed me to the next world. I can still remember how gladly I stretched myself out on this pallet for the first time. Never did the mountains listen to such songs from me as these shadowy walls did then.

"I had been glad to live and I was glad to die. Before I stepped aboard, I joyfully flung away my wretched load of ammunition, my knapsack, my hunting rifle that I had always been proud to carry, and I slipped into my winding sheet like a girl into her marriage dress. I lay and waited. Then came the mishap."

"A terrible fate," said the Burgomaster, raising his hand defensively. "And you bear no blame for it?"

"None," said the hunter. "I was a hunter; was there any sin in that? I following my calling as a hunter in the Black Forest, where there were still wolves in those days. I lay in ambush, shot, hit my mark, flayed the skins from my victims: was there any sin in that? My labours were blessed. 'The great hunter of the Black Forest' was the name I was given. Was there any sin in that?"

"I am not called upon to decide that," said the Burgomaster, "but to me also there seems to be no sin in such things. But, then whose is the guilt?"

"The boatman's," said the hunter. "Nobody will read what I say here, no one will come to help me; even if all the people were commanded to help me, every door and window would remain shut, everybody would take to bed and draw the bedclothes over his head, the whole earth would become an inn for the night. And there is sense in that, for nobody knows of me, and if anyone knew he would not know where I could be found, and if he knew where I could be found, he would not know how to deal with me, he would not know how to help me. The thought of helping me is an illness that has to be cured by taking to one's bed.

"I know that, and so I do not shout to summon help, even though at moments—when I lose control over myself, as I have done just now, for instance—I think seriously of it. But to drive out such thoughts I need only look round me and verify where I am, and—I can safely assert—have been for hundreds of years."

"Extraordinary," said the Burgomaster, "extraordinary.—And now do you think of staying here in Riva with us?"

"I think not," said the hunter with a smile, and, to excuse himself, he laid his hand on the Burgomaster's knee. "I am here, more than that I do not know, further than that I cannot go. My ship has no rudder, and it is driven by the wind that blows in the undermost regions of death."

Questions for Discussion

1. "The Hunter Gracchus" is an allegory in which the characters and events are representative of abstractions. Caroline Gordon and Allen Tate in their anthology *The House of Fiction* see the Hunter as Christ crucified but unable to enter Heaven, the boatman as the Church, the burgomaster as the Soul, the Dove as the Holy Spirit. What details justify such an interpretation? What final meaning do you derive from it?

2. How do the details in the beginning of the story prepare for the coming of the Hunter?

3. What is meant by the Hunter's statement: "I am forever . . . on the great stair that leads up to it"? How is it related to the last sentence of the story?

4. Why do you think the main character is made a hunter? What part does the concept of hunting play in the story?

5. Contrast the Hunter in the story with the hero of "St. Julian" and the hero of "The Rime of the Ancient Mariner." In what sense are they all guilty of unknown crimes for which they must suffer? In what sense are they suitable for romance?

Walter de la Mare (1873–1956)

The Listeners

"Is there anybody there?" said the Traveller,
  Knocking on the moonlit door;
And his horse in the silence champed the grasses
  Of the forest's ferny floor:
And a bird flew up out of the turret,
  Above the Traveller's head:
And he smote upon the door again a second time;
  "Is there anybody there?" he said.
But no one descended to the Traveller;
  No head from the leaf-fringed sill   10
Leaned over and looked into his gray eyes,
  Where he stood perplexed and still.
But only a host of phantom listeners
  That dwelt in the lone house then
Stood listening in the quiet of the moonlight
  To that voice from the world of men:
Stood thronging the faint moonbeams on the dark stair,
  That goes down to the empty hall,
Hearkening in an air stirred and shaken
  By the lonely Traveller's call.   20
And he felt in his heart their strangeness,
  Their stillness answering his cry,
While his horse moved, cropping the dark turf,
  'Neath the starred and leafy sky;
For he suddenly smote on the door, even
  Louder, and lifted his head:—
"Tell them I came, and no one answered,
  That I kept my word," he said.
Never the least stir made the listeners,
  Though every word he spake   30

Fell echoing through the shadowiness of the still house
   From the one man left awake:
Ay, they heard his foot upon the stirrup,
   And the sound of iron on stone,
And how the silence surged softly backward,
   When the plunging hoofs were gone.

Questions for Discussion

1. What are the ballad characteristics of "The Listeners"?

2. Does the poem in any way tell a story? Explain.

3. In what way can "The Listeners" be related to "La Belle Dame Sans Merci" as a romance?

4. How are the world of reality and the world of phantoms contrasted?

5. Explain the effectiveness of the last two lines with regard to the experience of the poem.

Robert Frost (1874–1963)

The Witch of Coös[1]

I stayed the night for shelter at a farm
Behind the mountain, with a mother and son,
Two old-believers. They did all the talking.

MOTHER. Folks think a witch who has familiar spirits
She could call up to pass a winter evening,
But won't, should be burned at the stake or something.
Summoning spirits isn't 'Button, button,
Who's got the button,' I would have them know.

SON. Mother can make a common table rear
And kick with two legs like an army mule.   10

MOTHER. And when I've done it, what good have I done?
Rather than tip a table for you, let me
Tell you what Ralle the Sioux Control once told me.
He said the dead had souls, but when I asked him
How could that be—I thought the dead were souls,
He broke my trance. Don't that make you suspicious
That there's something the dead are keeping back?
Yes, there's something the dead are keeping back.

SON. You wouldn't want to tell him what we have
Up attic, mother?   20

MOTHER. Bones—a skeleton.

1 A county in northern New Hampshire.

209

SON. But the headboard of mother's bed is pushed
Against the attic door: the door is nailed.
It's harmless. Mother hears it in the night
Halting perplexed behind the barrier
Of door and headboard. Where it wants to get
Is back into the cellar where it came from.

MOTHER. We'll never let them, will we, son! We'll never!

SON. It left the cellar forty years ago
And carried itself like a pile of dishes   30
Up one flight from the cellar to the kitchen,
Another from the kitchen to the bedroom,
Another from the bedroom to the attic,
Right past both father and mother, and neither stopped it.
Father had gone upstairs; mother was downstairs.
I was a baby: I don't know where I was.

MOTHER. The only fault my husband found with me—
I went to sleep before I went to bed,
Especially in winter when the bed
Might just as well be ice and the clothes snow.   40
The night the bones came up the cellar-stairs
Toffile had gone to bed alone and left me,
But left an open door to cool the room off
So as to sort of turn me out of it.
I was just coming to myself enough
To wonder where the cold was coming from,
When I heard Toffile upstairs in the bedroom
And thought I heard him downstairs in the cellar.
The board we had laid down to walk dry-shod on
When there was water in the cellar in spring   50
Struck the hard cellar bottom. And then someone
Began the stairs, two footsteps for each step,
The way a man with one leg and a crutch,
Or a little child, comes up. It wasn't Toffile:
It wasn't anyone who could be there.
The bulkhead double-doors were double-locked
And swollen tight and buried under snow.
The cellar windows were banked up with sawdust

And swollen tight and buried under snow.
It was the bones. I knew them—and good reason. 60
My first impulse was to get to the knob
And hold the door. But the bones didn't try
The door; they halted helpless on the landing,
Waiting for things to happen in their favor.
The faintest restless rustling ran all through them.
I never could have done the thing I did
If the wish hadn't been too strong in me
To see how they were mounted for this walk.
I had a vision of them put together
Not like a man, but like a chandelier. 70
So suddenly I flung the door wide on him.
A moment he stood balancing with emotion,
And all but lost himself. (A tongue of fire
Flashed out and licked along his upper teeth.
Smoke rolled inside the sockets of his eyes.)
Then he came at me with one hand outstretched,
The way he did in life once; but this time
I struck the hand off brittle on the floor,
And fell back from him on the floor myself.
The finger-pieces slid in all directions. 80
(Where did I see one of those pieces lately?
Hand me my button-box—it must be there.)
I sat up on the floor and shouted, 'Toffile,
It's coming up to you.' It had its choice
Of the door to the cellar or the hall.
It took the hall door for the novelty,
And set off briskly for so slow a thing,
Still going every which way in the joints, though,
So that it looked like lightning or a scribble,
From the slap I had just now given its hand. 90
I listened till it almost climbed the stairs
From the hall to the only finished bedroom,
Before I got up to do anything;
Then ran and shouted, 'Shut the bedroom door,
Toffile, for my sake!' 'Company?' he said,
'Don't make me get up; I'm too warm in bed.'
So lying forward weakly on the handrail
I pushed myself upstairs, and in the light
(The kitchen had been dark) I had to own
I could see nothing. 'Toffile, I don't see it. 100

It's with us in the room though. It's the bones.'
'What bones?' 'The cellar bones—out of the grave.'
That made him throw his bare legs out of bed
And sit up by me and take hold of me.
I wanted to put out the light and see
If I could see it, or else mow the room,
With our arms at the level of our knees,
And bring the chalk-pile down. 'I'll tell you what—
It's looking for another door to try.
The uncommonly deep snow has made him think   110
Of his old song, *The Wild Colonial Boy*,
He always used to sing along the tote road.
He's after an open door to get outdoors.
Let's trap him with an open door up attic.'
Toffile agreed to that, and sure enough,
Almost the moment he was given an opening,
The steps began to climb the attic stairs.
I heard them. Toffile didn't seem to hear them.
'Quick!' I slammed to the door and held the knob.
'Toffile, get nails.' I made him nail the door shut   120
And push the headboard of the bed against it.
Then we asked was there anything
Up attic that we'd ever want again.
The attic was less to us than the cellar.
If the bones liked the attic, let them have it.
Let them stay in the attic. When they sometimes
Come down the stairs at night and stand perplexed
Behind the door and headboard of the bed,
Brushing their chalky skull with chalky fingers,
With sounds like the dry rattling of a shutter,   130
That's what I sit up in the dark to say—
To no one any more since Toffile died.
Let them stay in the attic since they went there.
I promised Toffile to be cruel to them
For helping them be cruel once to him.

SON. We think they had a grave down in the cellar.

MOTHER. We know they had a grave down in the cellar.

SON. We never could find out whose bones they were.

MOTHER. Yes, we could too, son. Tell the truth for once.
They were a man's his father killed for me.   140
I mean a man he killed instead of me.
The least I could do was to help dig their grave.
We were about it one night in the cellar.
Son knows the story: but 'twas not for him
To tell the truth, suppose the time had come.
Son looks surprised to see me end a lie
We'd kept all these years between ourselves
So as to have it ready for outsiders.
But tonight I don't care enough to lie—
I don't remember why I ever cared.   150
Toffile, if he were here, I don't believe
Could tell you why he ever cared himself. . . .

She hadn't found the finger-bone she wanted
Among the buttons poured out in her lap.
I verified the name next morning: Toffile.
The rural letter box said Toffile Lajway.

Questions for Discussion

1. Why does the speaker call the mother and son "old believers"?

2. What is the basic situation in the poem?

3. Is this fundamentally a ghost story? How can the events in the poem be accounted for in natural rather than supernatural terms?

4. Contrast the attitude of the Mother and the Son toward the main situation. Is it true as one critic has stated that she sees in him "the side of herself that has kept her secret so many years"?

5. Toffile is the Canadian-French corruption of Théophile meaning the "Beloved of God." Teufel is the German word for devil. Explain how this ambivalence fits the poem.

6. To what extent can the poem be called comic despite its grisly subject matter?

Elizabeth Bowen (1899–   )

The Demon Lover

Towards the end of her day in London Mrs. Drover went round to her shut-up house to look for several things she wanted to take away. Some belonged to herself, some to her family, who were by now used to their country life. It was late August; it had been a steamy, showery day: at the moment the trees down the pavement glittered in an escape of humid yellow afternoon sun. Against the next batch of clouds, already piling up ink-dark, broken chimneys and parapets stood out. In her once familiar street, as in any unused channel, an unfamiliar queerness had silted up; a cat wove itself in and out of railings, but no human eye watched Mrs. Drover's return. Shifting some parcels under her arm, she slowly forced round her latchkey in an unwilling lock, then gave the door, which had warped, a push with her knee. Dead air came out to meet her as she went in.

The staircase window having been boarded up, no light came down into the hall. But one door, she could just see, stood ajar, so she went quickly through into the room and unshuttered the big window in there. Now the prosaic woman, looking about her, was more perplexed than she knew by everything that she saw, by traces of her long former habit of life—the yellow smoke-stain up the white marble mantelpiece, the ring left by a vase on the top of the escritoire; the bruise in the wallpaper where, on the door being thrown open widely, the china handle had always hit the wall. The piano, having gone away to be stored, had left what looked like claw-marks on its part of the parquet. Though not much dust had seeped in, each object wore a film of another kind; and, the only ventilation being the chimney, the whole drawing-room smelled of the cold hearth. Mrs. Drover put down her parcels on the escritoire and left the room to proceed upstairs; the things she wanted were in a bedroom chest.

She had been anxious to see how the house was—the part-time caretaker she shared with some neighbours was away this week on his holiday, known to be not yet back. At the best of times he did not look in often, and she was never sure that she trusted him. There were some cracks in the structure, left by the last bombing, on which she was anxious to keep an eye. Not that one could do anything—

A shaft of refracted daylight now lay across the hall. She stopped dead and stared at the hall table—on this lay a letter addressed to her.

She thought first—then the caretaker *must* be back. All the same, who, seeing the house shuttered, would have dropped a letter in at the box? It was not a circular, it was not a bill. And the post office redirected, to the address in the country, everything for her that came through the post. The caretaker (even if he *were* back) did not know she was due in London to-day—her call here had been planned to be a surprise—so his negligence in the matter of this letter, leaving it to wait in the dusk and the dust, annoyed her. Annoyed, she picked up the letter, which bore no stamp. But it cannot be important, or they would know. . . . She took the letter rapidly upstairs with her, without a stop to look at the writing till she reached what had been her bedroom, where she let in light. The room looked over the garden and other gardens: the sun had gone in; as the clouds sharpened and lowered, the trees and rank lawns seemed already to smoke with dark. Her reluctance to look again at the letter came from the fact that she felt intruded upon—and by someone contemptuous of her ways. However, in the tenseness preceding the fall of rain she read it: it was a few lines.

DEAR KATHLEEN,

You will not have forgotten that to-day is our anniversary, and the day we said. The years have gone by at once slowly and fast. In view of the fact that nothing has changed, I shall rely upon you to keep your promise. I was sorry to see you leave London, but was satisfied that you would be back in time. You may expect me, therefore, at the hour arranged.

Until then . . .

K.

Mrs. Drover looked for the date: it was to-day's. She dropped the letter on to the bed-springs, then picked it up to see the writing again—her lips, beneath the remains of lipstick, beginning to go white. She felt so much the change in her own face that she went to the mirror, polished a clear patch in it and looked at once urgently and stealthily in. She was confronted by a woman of forty-four, with eyes starting out under a hatbrim that had been rather carelessly pulled down. She had not put on any more powder since she left the shop where she ate her solitary tea. The pearls her husband had given her on their marriage hung loose round her now rather thinner throat, slipping into the V of the pink wool jumper her sister knitted last autumn as they sat round the fire. Mrs. Drover's most normal expression was one of controlled worry, but of assent. Since the birth of the third of her little boys, attended by a quite serious illness, she had had an intermittent muscular flicker to the left of her mouth, but in spite of this she could always sustain a manner that was at once energetic and calm.

Turning from her own face as precipitately as she had gone to meet it, she went to the chest where the things were, unlocked it, threw up the lid and knelt to search. But as rain began to come crashing down she could not keep from looking over her shoulder at the stripped bed on which the letter lay. Behind the blanket of rain the clock of the church that still stood struck six—with rapidly heightening apprehension she counted each of the slow strokes. "The hour arranged. . . . My God," she said *"what* hour? How should I . . . ? After twenty-five years. . . ."

The young girl talking to the soldier in the garden had not ever completely seen his face. It was dark; they were saying good-bye under a tree. Now and then—for it felt, from not seeing him at this intense moment, as though she had never seen him at all—she verified his presence for these few moments longer by putting out a hand, which he each time pressed, without very much kindness, and painfully, on to one of the breast buttons of his uniform. That cut of the button on the palm of her hand was, principally, what she was to carry away. This was so near the end of a leave from France that she could only wish him already gone. It was August 1916. Being not kissed, being drawn away from and looked at intimidated Kathleen till she imagined spectral glitters in the place of his eyes. Turning away and looking back up the lawn she saw, through branches of trees, the drawing-room window alight: she caught a breath for the moment when she could go running back there into the safe arms of her mother and sister, and cry: "What shall I do, what shall I do? He has gone."

Hearing her catch her breath, her fiancé said, without feeling: "Cold?"

"You're going away such a long way."

"Not so far as you think."

"I don't understand?"

"You don't have to," he said. "You will. You know what we said."

"But that was—suppose you—I mean, suppose."

"I shall be with you," he said, "sooner or later. You won't forget that. You need do nothing but wait."

Only a little more than a minute later she was free to run up the silent lawn. Looking in through the window at her mother and sister, who did not for the moment perceive her, she already felt that unnatural promise drive down between her and the rest of all human kind. No other way of having given herself could have made her feel so apart, lost and foresworn. She could not have plighted a more sinister troth.

Kathleen behaved well when, some months later, her fiancé was reported missing, presumed killed. Her family not only supported her but were able to praise her courage without stint because they could not regret, as a husband for her, the man they knew almost nothing about. They hoped she would, in a year or two, console herself—and had it been only a question of consolation things might have gone much straighter ahead. But her trouble, behind just a little grief, was a complete dislocation from everything. She did not reject other lovers, for these failed to appear: for years she failed to attract men—and with the approach of her thirties she became natural enough to share her family's anxiousness on this score. She began to put herself out, to wonder; and at thirty-two she was very greatly relieved to find herself being courted by William Drover. She married him, and the two of them settled down in this quiet, arboreal part of Kensington: in this house the years piled up, her children were born and they all lived till they were driven out by the bombs of the next war. Her movements as Mrs. Drover were circumscribed, and she dismissed any idea that they were still watched.

As things were—dead or living the letter-writer sent her only a threat. Unable, for some minutes, to go on kneeling with her back exposed to the empty room, Mrs. Drover rose from the chest to sit on an upright chair whose back was firmly against the wall. The desuetude of her former bedroom, her married London home's whole air of being a cracked cup from which memory, with its reassuring power, had either evaporated or leaked away, made a crisis—and at just this crisis the letter-writer had, knowledgeably, struck. The hollowness of the house this evening cancelled years on years of voices, habits and steps. Through the shut windows she only heard rain fall on the roofs around. To rally herself, she said she was in a mood—and, for two or three seconds shutting her eyes, told herself that she had imagined the letter. But she opened them—there it lay on the bed.

On the supernatural side of the letter's entrance she was not permitting her mind to dwell. Who, in London, knew she meant to call at the house today? Evidently, however, this had been known. The caretaker, *had* he come back, had had no cause to expect her: he would have taken the letter in his pocket, to forward it, at his own time, through the post. There was no other sign that the caretaker had been in—but, if not? Letters dropped in at doors of deserted houses do not fly or walk to tables in halls. They do not sit on the dust of empty tables with the air of certainty that they will be found. There is needed some human hand—but nobody but the caretaker had a key. Under circumstances she did not care to consider, a house can be entered without a key. It was possible that she was not alone now. She might be being waited for, downstairs. Waited for—until when? Until "the hour arranged." At least that was not six o'clock: six had struck.

She rose from the chair and went over and locked the door.

The thing was, to get out. To fly? No, not that: she had to catch her train. As a woman whose utter dependability was the keystone of her family life she was not willing to return to the country, to her husband, her little boys and her sister, without the objects she had come up to fetch. Resuming work at the chest she set about making up a number of parcels in a rapid, fumbling-decisive way. These, with her shopping parcels, would be too much to carry; these meant a taxi—at the thought of the taxi her heart went up and her normal breathing resumed. I will ring up the taxi now; the taxi cannot come too soon: I shall hear the taxi out there running its engine, till I walk calmly down to it through the hall. I'll ring up—But no: the telephone is cut off. . . . She tugged at a knot she had tied wrong.

The idea of flight . . . He was never kind to me, not really. I don't remember him kind at all. Mother said he never considered me. He was set on me, that was what it was—not love. Not love, not meaning a person well. What did he do, to make me promise like that? I can't remember— But she found that she could.

She remembered with such dreadful acuteness that the twenty-five years since then dissolved like smoke and she instinctively looked for the weal left by the button on the palm of her hand. She remembered not only all that he said and did but the complete suspension of *her* existence during that August week. I was not myself—they all told me so at the time. She remembered—but with one white burning blank as where acid has dropped on a photograph: *under no conditions* could she remember his face.

So, wherever he may be waiting, I shall not know him. You have no time to run from a face you do not expect.

The thing was to get to the taxi before any clock struck what could be the hour. She would slip down the street and round the side of the square to where the square gave on the main road. She would return in the taxi, safe, to her own door, and bring the solid driver into the house with her to pick up the parcels from room to room. The idea of the taxi driver made her decisive, bold: she unlocked her door, went to the top of the staircase and listened down.

She heard nothing—but while she was hearing nothing the *passé* air of the staircase was disturbed by a draught that travelled up to her face. It emanated from the basement: down there a door or window was being opened by someone who chose this moment to leave the house.

The rain had stopped; the pavements steamily shone as Mrs. Drover let herself out by inches from her own front door into the empty street. The unoccupied houses opposite continued to meet her look with their damaged stare. Making towards the thoroughfare and the taxi, she tried not to keep looking behind. Indeed, the silence was so intense—one of those creeks of London silence exaggerated this summer by the damage of war—that no tread could have gained on hers unheard. Where her street debouched on the square where people went on living she grew conscious of and checked her unnatural pace. Across the open end of the square two buses impassively passed each other; women, a perambulator, cyclists, a man wheeling a barrow signalized, once again, the ordinary flow of life. At the square's most populous corner should be—and was—the short taxi rank. This evening, only one taxi—but this, although it presented its blank rump, appeared already to be alertly waiting for her. Indeed, without looking round the driver started the engine as she panted up from behind and put her hand on the door. As she did so, the clock struck seven. The taxi faced the main road: to make the trip back to her house it would have to turn—she had settled back on the seat and the taxi *had* turned before she, surprised by its knowing movement, recollected that she had not "said where." She leaned forward to scratch at the glass panel that divided the driver's head from her own.

The driver braked to what was almost a stop, turned round and slid the glass panel back: the jolt of this flung Mrs. Drover forward till her face was almost into the glass. Through the aperture driver and passenger, not six inches between them, remained for an eternity eye to eye. Mrs. Drover's mouth hung open for some seconds before she could issue her first scream. After that she continued to scream freely and to beat with her gloved hands on the glass all round as the taxi, accelerating without mercy, made off with her into the hinterland of deserted streets.

Questions for Discussion

1. Compare the situation in this story with that in the ballad of the same name. Of what importance is the setting in the London of World War II?

2. How do Mrs. Drover's circumstances and state of mind prepare you for the sudden revelation at the end?

3. Is Mrs. Drover alone in the house? Explain the presence of the letter. Is it caused by a supernatural force?

4. Characterize the lover. What is meant by Mrs. Drover's thinking that he was "set" on her but did not love her? What is the significance of her remembering the cut of his button on her palm?

5. Explain the appropriateness of the ending. Why is the word *hinterland* used in the last sentence?

6. Would you characterize the story as Gothic in the same way that you would "William Wilson"?

Truman Capote (1924–   )

The Headless Hawk

They are of those that rebel against the light; they know not the ways there-of, nor abide in the paths thereof. In the dark they dig through houses, which they had marked for themselves in the daytime: they know not the light. For the morning is to them as the shadow of death: if one know them, they are in the terrors of the shadow of death.   —JOB 24: 13, 16, 17

Vincent switched off the lights in the gallery. Outside, after locking the door, he smoothed the brim of an elegant Panama, and started toward Third Avenue, his umbrella-cane tap-tap-tapping along the pavement. A promise of rain had darkened the day since dawn, and a sky of bloated clouds blurred the five o'clock sun; it was hot, though, humid as tropical mist, and voices, sounding along the gray July street, sounding muffled and strange, carried a fretful undertone. Vincent felt as though he moved below the sea. Buses, cruising crosstown through Fifty-seventh Street, seemed like green-bellied fish, and faces loomed and rocked like wave-riding masks. He studied each passer-by, hunting one, and presently he saw her, a girl in a green raincoat. She was standing on the downtown corner of Fifty-seventh and Third, just standing there smoking a cigarette, and giving somehow the impression she hummed a tune. The raincoat was transparent. She wore dark slacks, no socks, a pair of huaraches, a man's white shirt. Her hair was fawn-colored, and cut like a boy's. When she noticed Vincent crossing toward her, she dropped the cigarette and hurried down the block to the doorway of an antique store.

Vincent slowed his step. He pulled out a handkerchief and dabbed his forehead; if only he could get away, go up to the Cape, lie in the sun. He

"The Headless Hawk" by Truman Capote. From *A Tree of Night and Other Stories,* by Truman Capote. Reprinted by permission of Random House, Inc.

bought an afternoon paper, and fumbled his change. It rolled in the gutter, dropped silently out of sight down a sewer grating. "Ain't but a nickel, bub," said the news-dealer, for Vincent, though actually unaware of his loss, looked heartbroken. And it was like that often now, never quite in contact, never sure whether a step would take him backward or forward, up or down. Very casually, with the handle of the umbrella hooked over an arm, and his eyes concentrated on the paper's headlines—but what did the damn thing say? —he continued downtown. A swarthy woman carrying a shopping bag jostled him, glared, muttered in coarsely vehement Italian. The ragged cut of her voice seemed to come through layers of wool. As he approached the antique store where the girl in the green raincoat waited, he walked slower still, counting one, two, three, four, five, six—at six he halted before the window.

The window was like a corner of an attic; a lifetime's discardings rose in a pyramid of no particular worth: vacant picture frames, a lavender wig, Gothic shaving mugs, beaded lamps. There was an oriental mask suspended on a ceiling cord, and wind from an electric fan whirling inside the shop revolved it slowly round and round. Vincent, by degrees, lifted his gaze, and looked at the girl directly. She was hovering in the doorway so that he saw her greenness distorted wavy through double glass; the elevated pounded overhead and the window trembled. Her image spread like a reflection on silverware, then gradually hardened again: she was watching him.

He hung an Old Gold between his lips, rummaged for a match and, finding none, sighed. The girl stepped from the doorway. She held out a cheap little lighter; as the flame pulsed up, her eyes, pale, shallow, cat-green, fixed him with alarming intensity. Her eyes had an astonished, a shocked look, as though, having at one time witnessed a terrible incident, they'd locked wide open. Carefree bangs fringed her forehead; this boy haircut emphasized the childish and rather poetic quality of her narrow, hollow-checked face. It was the kind of face one sometimes sees in paintings of medieval youths.

Letting the smoke pour out his nose, Vincent, knowing it was useless to ask, wondered, as always, what she was living on, and where. He flipped away the cigarette, for he had not wanted it to begin with, and then, pivoting, crossed rapidly under the El; as he approached the curb he heard a crash of brakes and suddenly, as if cotton plugs had been blasted from his ears, city noises crowded in. A cab driver hollered: "Fa crissake, sistuh, get the lead outa yuh pants!" but the girl did not even bother turning her head; trance-eyed, undisturbed as a sleepwalker, and staring straight at Vincent, who watched dumbly, she moved across the street. A colored boy wearing a jazzy purple suit took her elbow. "You sick, Miss?" he said, guiding her forward,

and she did not answer. "You look mighty funny, Miss. If you sick, I . . ."
then, following the direction of her eyes, he released his hold. There was
something here which made him all still inside. "Uh—yeah," he muttered,
backing off with a grinning display of tartar-coated teeth.

So Vincent began walking in earnest, and his umbrella tapped code-
like block after block. His shirt was soaked through with itchy sweat, and
the noises, now so harsh, banged in his head: a trick car horn hooting "My
Country, 'Tis of Thee," electric spray of sparks crackling bluely off thunder-
ing rails, whiskey laughter hiccuping through gaunt doors of beer-stale
bars where orchid juke machines manufactured U.S.A. music—"I got spurs
that jingle jangle jingle. . . . " Occasionally he caught a glimpse of her, once
mirrored in the window of Paul's Seafood Palace where scarlet lobsters
basked on a beach of flaked ice. She followed close with her hands shoved
into the pockets of her raincoat. The brassy lights of a movie marquee
blinked, and he remembered how she loved movies: murder films, spy chil-
lers, Wild West shows. He turned into a side street leading toward the East
River; it was quiet here, hushed like Sunday: a sailor-stroller munching an
Eskimo pie, energetic twins skipping rope, an old velvety lady with gardenia-
white hair lifting aside lace curtains and peering listlessly into rain-dark
space—a city landscape in July. And behind him the soft insistent slap of
sandals. Traffic lights on Second Avenue turned red; at the corner a bearded
midget, Ruby the Popcorn Man, wailed, "Hot buttered popcorn, big bag,
yah?" Vincent shook his head, and the midget looked very put out, then:
"Yuh see?" he jeered, pushing a shovel inside of the candlelit cage where
bursting kernels bounced like crazy moths. "Yuh see, de girlie knows popcorn's nourishin'." She bought a dime's worth, and it was in a green sack
matching her raincoat, matching her eyes.

This is my neighborhood, my street, the house with the gateway is
where I live. To remind himself of this was necessary, inasmuch as he'd
substituted for a sense of reality a knowledge of time, and place. He glanced
gratefully at sourfaced, faded ladies, at the pipe-puffing males squatting on
the surrounding steps of brownstone stoops. Nine pale little girls shrieked
round a corner flower cart begging daisies to pin in their hair, but the peddler
said, "Shoo!" and, fleeing like beads of a broken bracelet, they circled in
the street, the wild ones leaping with laughter, and the shy ones, silent and
isolated, lifting summer-wilted faces skyward: the rain, would it never come?

Vincent, who lived in a basement apartment, descended several steps
and took out his keycase; then, pausing behind the hallway door, he looked
back through a peephole in the paneling. The girl was waiting on the side-
walk above; she leaned against a brownstone banister, and her arms fell limp
—and popcorn spilled snowlike round her feet. A grimy little boy crept slyly
up to pick among it like a squirrel.

II

For Vincent it was a holiday. No one had come by the gallery all morning, which, considering the arctic weather, was not unusual. He sat at his
desk devouring tangerines, and enjoying immensely a Thurber story in an
old *New Yorker*. Laughing loudly, he did not hear the girl enter, see her cross
the dark carpet, notice her at all, in fact, until the telephone rang. "Garland
Gallery, hello." She was odd, most certainly, that indecent haircut, those
depthless eyes—"Oh Paul, *Comme ci, comme ça*, and you?"—and dressed
like a freak: no coat, just a lumberjack's shirt, navy-blue slacks and—was it a
joke?—pink ankle socks, a pair of huaraches. "The ballet? Who's dancing?
Oh, her!" Under an arm she carried a flat parcel wrapped in sheets of funny-
paper—"Look, Paul, what say I call back? There's someone here . . ." and,
anchoring the receiver, assuming a commercial smile, he stood up. "Yes?"

Her lips, crusty with chap, trembled with unrealized words as though
she had possibly a defect of speech, and her eyes rolled in their sockets like
loose marbles. It was the kind of disturbed shyness one associates with children. "I've a picture," she said. "You buy pictures?"

At this, Vincent's smile became fixed. "We exhibit."

"I painted it myself," she said, and her voice, hoarse and slurred, was
Southern. "My picture—I painted it. A lady told me there were places
around here that bought pictures."

Vincent said, "Yes, of course, but the truth is"—and he made a helpless
gesture—"the truth is I've no authority whatever. Mr. Garland—this is his
gallery, you know—is out of town." Standing there on the expanse of fine
carpet, her body sagging sideways with the weight of her package, she
looked like a sad rag doll. "Maybe," he began, "maybe Henry Krueger up the
street at Sixty-five . . ." but she was not listening.

"I did it myself," she insisted softly. "Tuesdays and Thursdays were our
painting days, and a whole year I worked. The others, they kept messing
it up, and Mr. Destronelli . . ." Suddenly, as though aware of an indiscretion,
she stopped and bit her lip. Her eyes narrowed. "He's not a friend of
yours?"

"Who?" said Vincent, confused.

"Mr. Destronelli."

He shook his head, and wondered why it was that eccentricity always
excited in him such curious admiration. It was the feeling he'd had as a child
toward carnival freaks. And it was true that about those whom he'd loved
there was always a little something wrong, broken. Strange, though, that
this quality, having stimulated an attraction, should, in his case, regularly
end it by destroying it. "Of course I haven't any authority," he repeated,

sweeping tangerine hulls into a wastebasket, "but, if you like, I suppose I could look at your work."

A pause; then, kneeling on the floor, she commenced stripping off the funny-paper wrapping. It originally had been, Vincent noticed, part of the New Orleans *Times-Picayune.* "From the South, aren't you?" he said. She did not look up, but he saw her shoulders stiffen. "No," she said. Smiling, he considered a moment, decided it would be tactless to challenge so transparent a lie. Or could she have misunderstood? And all at once he felt an intense longing to touch her head, finger her boyish hair. He shoved his hands in his pockets and glanced at the window. It was spangled with February frost, and some passer-by had scratched on the glass an obscenity.

"There," she said.

A headless figure in a monklike robe reclined complacently on top a tacky vaudeville trunk; in one hand she held a fuming blue candle, in the other a miniature gold cage, and her severed head lay bleeding at her feet: it was the girl's, this head, but here her hair was long, very long, and a snowball kitten with crystal spitfire eyes playfully pawed, as it would a spool of yarn, the sprawling ends. The wings of a hawk, headless, scarlet-breasted, copper-clawed, curtained the background like a nightfall sky. It was a crude painting, the hard pure colors molded with male brutality, and, while there was not technical merit evident, it had that power often seen in something deeply felt, though primitively conveyed. Vincent reacted as he did when occasionally a phrase of music surprised a note of inward recognition, or a cluster of words in a poem revealed to him a secret concerning himself: he felt a powerful chill of pleasure run down his spine. "Mr. Garland is in Florida," he said cautiously, "but I think he should see it; you couldn't leave it for, say, a week?"

"I had a ring and I sold it," she said, and he had the feeling she was talking in a trance. "It was a nice ring, a wedding ring—not mine—with writing on it. I had an overcoat, too." She twisted one of her shirt buttons, pulled till it popped off and rolled on the carpet like a pearl eye. "I don't want much—fifty dollars; is that unfair?"

"Too much," said Vincent, more curtly than he intended. Now he wanted her painting, not for the gallery, but for himself. There are certain works of art which excite more interest in their creators than in what they have created, usually because in this kind of work one is able to identify something which has until that instant seemed a private inexpressible perception, and you wonder: who is this that knows me, and how? "I'll give thirty."

For a moment she gaped at him stupidly, and then, sucking her breath, held out her hand, palm up. This directness, too innocent to be offensive, caught him off guard. Somewhat embarrassed, he said, "I'm most awfully afraid I'll have to mail a check. Could you . . . ?" The telephone interrupted, and, as he went to answer, she followed, her hand outstretched, a frantic look pinching her face. "Oh, Paul, may I call back? Oh, I see. Well, hold on a sec." Cupping the mouthpiece against his shoulder, he pushed a pad and pencil across the desk. "Here, write your name and address."

But she shook her head, the dazed, anxious expression deepening.

"Check," said Vincent, "I have to mail a check. Please, your name and address." He grinned encouragely when at last she began to write.

"Sorry, Paul . . . Whose party? Why, the little bitch, she didn't invite . . . Hey!" he called, for the girl was moving toward the door. "Please, hey!" Cold air chilled the gallery, and the door slammed with a glassy rattle. Hello-hellohello. Vincent did not answer; he stood puzzling over the curious information she'd left printed on his pad: D. J.—Y.W.C.A. Hellohellohello.

It hung above his mantel, the painting, and on those nights when he could not sleep he would pour a glass of whiskey and talk to the headless hawk, tell it the stuff of his life: he was, he said, a poet who had never written poetry, a painter who had never painted, a lover who had never loved (absolutely)—someone, in short, without direction, and quite headless. Oh, it wasn't that he hadn't tried—good beginnings, always, bad endings, always. Vincent, white, male, age 36, college graduate: a man in the sea, fifty miles from shore; a victim, born to be murdered, either by himself or another; an actor unemployed. It was there, all of it, in the painting, everything disconnected and cockeyed, and who was she that she should know so much? Inquiries, those he'd made, had led nowhere, not another dealer knew of her, and to search for a D. J. living in, presumably, a Y.W.C.A. seemed absurd. Then, too, he'd quite expected she would reappear, but February passed, and March. One evening, crossing the square which fronts the Plaza, he had a queer thing happen. The archaic hansom drivers who line that location were lighting their carriage lamps, for it was dusk, and lamplight traced through moving leaves. A hansom pulled from the curb and rolled past in the twilight. There was a single occupant, and this passenger, whose face he could not see, was a girl with chopped fawn-colored hair. So he settled on a bench, and whiled away time talking with a soldier, and a fairy colored boy who quoted poetry, and a man out airing a dachshund: night characters with whom he waited—but the carriage, with the one for whom he waited, never came back. Again he saw her (or supposed he did) descending subway stairs, and this time lost her in the tiled tunnels of painted arrows and Spearmint machines. It was as if her face were imposèd upon his mind; he could no more dispossess it than could, for example, a dead man rid his legendary eyes of the last image seen. Around the middle of April he went up to Connecticut to spend a weekend with his married sister; keyed-up, caustic, he wasn't, as she complained, at all like himself. "What is it, Vinny, darling —if you need money . . ." "Oh, shut up!" he said. "Must be love," teased his brother-in-law. "Come on, Vinny, 'fess up; what's she like?" And all this so annoyed him he caught the next train home. From a booth in Grand Central he called to apologize, but a sick nervousness hummed inside him, and he hung up while the operator was still trying to make a connection. He wanted a drink. At the Commodore Bar he spent an hour or so drowning four daiquiris—it was Saturday, it was nine, there was nothing to do unless he did it alone, he was feeling sad for himself. Now in the park behind the Public Library sweethearts moved whisperingly under trees, and drinking-fountain water bubbled softly, like their voices, but for all the white April evening meant to him, Vincent, drunk a little and wandering, might as well have been old, like the old bench-sitters rasping phlegm.

In the country, spring is a time of small happenings happening quietly, hyacinth shoots thrusting in a garden, willows burning with a sudden frosty fire of green, lengthening afternoons of long flowing dusk, and midnight rain opening lilac; but in the city there is the fanfare of organ-grinders, and odors, undiluted by winter wind, clog the air; windows long closed go up, and conversation, drifting beyond a room, collides with the jangle of a peddler's bell. It is the crazy season of toy balloons and roller skates, of courtyard baritones and men of freakish enterprise, like the one who jumped up now like a jack-in-the-box. He was old, he had a telescope and a sign: 25¢ See the Moon! See the Stars! 25¢! No stars could penetrate a city's glare, but Vincent saw the moon, a round, shadowed whiteness, and then a blaze of electric bulbs: Four Roses, Bing Cro——he was moving through caramel-scented staleness, swimming through oceans of cheese-pale faces, neon, and darkness. Above the blasting of a jukebox, bulletfire boomed, a cardboard duck fell plop, and somebody screeched: "Yay Iggy!" It was a Broadway funhouse, a penny arcade, and jammed from wall to wall with Saturday splurgers. He watched a penny movie (*What The Bootblack Saw*), and had his fortune told by a wax witch leering behind glass: "Yours is an affectionate nature" . . . but he read no further, for up near the jukebox there was an attractive commotion. A crowd of kids, clapping in time to jazz music, had formed a circle around two dancers. These dancers were both colored, both girls. They swayed together slow and easy, like lovers, rocked and stamped and rolled serious savage eyes, their muscles rhythmically attuned to the ripple of a clarinet, the rising harangue of a drum. Vincent's gaze traveled round the audience, and when he saw her a bright shiver went through him, for something of the dance's violence was reflected in her face. Standing there beside a tall ugly boy, it was as if she were the sleeper and the Negroes a dream. Trumpet-drum-piano, bawling on behind a black girl's froggy voice, wailed toward a rocking finale. The clapping ended, the dancers parted. She was alone now; though Vincent's instinct was to leave before she noticed, he advanced, and, as one would gently waken a sleeper, lightly touched her shoulder. "Hello," he said, his voice too loud. Turning, she stared at him, and her eyes were clear-blank. First terror, then puzzlement replaced the dead lost look. She took a step backward, and, just as the jukebox commenced hollering again, he seized her wrist: "You remember me," he prompted, "the gallery? Your painting?" She blinked, let the lids sink sleepily over those eyes, and he could feel the slow relaxing of tension in her arm. She was thinner than he recalled, prettier, too, and her hair, grown out somewhat, hung in casual disorder. A little silver Christmas ribbon dangled sadly from a stray lock. He started to say, "Can I buy you a drink?" but she leaned against him, her head resting on his chest like a child's, and he said: "Will you come home with me?" She lifted her face; the answer, when it came, was a breath, a whisper: "Please," she said.

Vincent stripped off his clothes, arranged them neatly in the closet, and admired his nakedness before a mirrored door. He was not so handsome as he supposed, but handsome all the same. For his moderate height he was excellently proportioned; his hair was dark yellow, and his delicate, rather snub-nosed face had a fine, ruddy coloring. The rumble of running water broke the quiet; she was in the bathroom preparing to bathe. He dressed in loose-fitting flannel pajamas, lit a cigarette, said, "Everything all right?" The water went off, a long silence, then: "Yes, thank you." On the way home in a cab he'd made an attempt at conversation, but she had said nothing, not even when they entered the apartment—and this last offended him, for, taking rather female pride in his quarters, he'd expected a complimentary remark. It was one enormously high-ceilinged room, a bath and kitchenette, a backyard garden. In the furnishings he'd combined modern with antique and produced a distinguished result. Decorating the walls were a trio of Toulouse-Lautrec prints, a framed circus poster, D. J.'s painting, photographs of Rilke, Nijinsky and Duse. A candelabra of lean blue candles burned on a desk; the room, washed in their delirious light, wavered. French doors led into the yard. He never used it much, for it was a place impossible to keep clean. There were a few dead tulip stalks dark in the moonshine, a puny heaven tree, and an old weather-worn chair left by the last tenant. He paced back and forth over the cold flagstones, hoping that in the cool air the drugged drunk sensation he felt would wear off. Nearby a piano was being badly mauled, and in a window above there was a child's face. He was thumbing a blade of grass when her shadow fell long across the yard. She was in the doorway. "You mustn't come out," he said, moving toward her. "It's turned a little cold."

There was about her now an appealing softness; she seemed somehow less angular, less out of tune with the average, and Vincent, offering a glass of sherry, was delighted at the delicacy with which she touched it to her lips.

She was wearing his terry-cloth robe; it was by yards too large. Her feet were bare, and she tucked them up beside her on the couch. "It's like Glass Hill, the candlelight," she said, and smiled. "My Granny lived at Glass Hill. We had lovely times, sometimes; do you know what she used to say? She used to say, 'Candles are magic wands; light one and the world is a story book.' "

"What a dreary old lady she must've been," said Vincent, quite drunk. "We should probably have hated each other."

"Granny would've loved you," she said. "She loved any kind of man, every man she ever met, even Mr. Destronelli."

"Destronelli?" It was a name he'd heard before.

Her eyes slid slyly sideways, and this look seemed to say: There must be no subterfuge between us, we who understand each other have no need of it. "Oh, you know," she said with a conviction that, under more commonplace circumstances, would have been surprising. It was, however, as if he'd abandoned temporarily the faculty of surprise. "Everybody knows him."

He curved an arm around her, and brought her nearer. "Not me, I don't," he said, kissing her mouth, neck; she was not responsive especially, but he said—and his voice had gone adolescently shaky—"Never met Mr. Whoozits." He slipped a hand inside her robe, loosening it away from her shoulders. Above one breast she had a birthmark, small and star-shaped. He glanced at the mirrored door where uncertain light rippled their reflections, made them pale and incomplete. She was smiling. "Mr. Whoozits," he said, "what does he look like?" The suggestion of a smile faded, a small monkey-like frown flickered on her face. She looked above the mantel at her painting, and he realized that this was the first notice she'd shown it; she appeared to study in the picture a particular object, but whether hawk or head he could not say. "Well," she said quietly, pressing closer to him, "he looks like you, like me, like most anybody."

It was raining; in the wet noon light two nubs of candle still burned, and at an open window gray curtains tossed forlornly. Vincent extricated his arm; it was numb from the weight of her body. Careful not to make a noise, he eased out of bed, blew out the candles, tiptoed into the bathroom, and doused his face with cold water. On the way to the kitchenette he flexed his arms, feeling, as he hadn't for a long time, an intensely male pleasure in his strength, a healthy wholeness of person. He made and put on a tray orange juice, raisin-bread toast, a pot of tea; then, so inexpertly that everything on the tray rattled, he brought the breakfast in and placed it on a table beside the bed.

She had not moved; her ruffled hair spread fanwise across the pillow, and one hand rested in the hollow where his head had lain. He leaned over and kissed her lips, and her eyelids, blue with sleep, trembled. "Yes, yes, I'm awake," she murmured, and rain, lifting in the wind, sprayed against the

window like surf. He somehow knew that with her there would be none of
the usual artifice; no avoidance of eyes, no shamefaced, accusing pause. She
raised herself on her elbow; she looked at him, Vincent thought, as if he
were her husband, and, handing her the orange juice, he smiled his gratitude.

"What is today?"

"Sunday," he told her, bundling under the quilt, and settling the tray
across his legs.

"But there are no church bells," she said. "And it's raining."

Vincent divided a piece of toast. "You don't mind that, do you? Rain—
such a peaceful sound." He poured tea. "Sugar? Cream?"

She disregarded this, and said, "Today is Sunday what? What month,
I mean?"

"Where have you been living, in the subway?" he said, grinning. And it
puzzled him to think she was serious. "Oh, April . . . April something-or-
other."

"April," she repeated. "Have I been here long?"

"Only since last night."

"Oh."

Vincent stirred his tea, the spoon tinkling in the cup like a bell. Toast
crumbs spilled among the sheets, and he thought of the *Tribune* and the
Times waiting outside the door, but they, this morning, held no charms;
it was best lying there beside her in the warm bed, sipping tea, listening to
the rain. Odd, when you stopped to consider, certainly very odd. She did not
know his name, nor he hers. And so he said, "I still owe you thirty dollars,
do you realize that? Your own fault, of course—leaving such a damn fool
address. And D. J., what is that supposed to mean?"

"I don't think I'd better tell you my name," she said. "I could make up
one easy enough: Dorothy Jordan, Delilah Johnson; see? There are all kinds
of names I could make up, and if it wasn't for him I'd tell you right."

Vincent lowered the tray to the floor. He rolled over on his side, and,
facing her, his heartbeat quickened. "Who's him?" Though her expression
was calm, anger muddied her voice when she said, "If you don't know him,
then tell me, why am I here?"

Silence, and outside the rain seemed suddenly suspended. A ship's horn
moaned in the river. Holding her close, he combed his fingers through her
hair, and, wanting so much to be believed, said, "Because I love you."

She closed her eyes. "What became of them?"

"Who?"

"The others you've said that to."

It commenced again, the rain spattering grayly at the window, falling
on hushed Sunday streets; listening, Vincent remembered. He remembered his cousin, Lucille, poor, beautiful, stupid Lucille who sat all day em-

broidering silk flowers on scraps of linen. And Allen T. Baker—there was the winter they'd spent in Havana, the house they'd lived in, crumbling rooms of rose-colored rock; poor Allen, he'd thought it was to be forever. Gordon, too. Gordon, with the kinky yellow hair, and a head full of old Elizabethan ballads. Was it true he'd shot himself? And Connie Silver, the deaf girl, the one who had wanted to be an actress—what had become of her? Or Helen, Louise, Laura? "There was just one," he said, and to his own ears, this had a truthful ring. "Only one, and she's dead."

Tenderly, as if in sympathy, she touched his cheek. "I suppose he killed her," she said, her eyes so close he could see the outline of his face imprisoned in their greenness. "He killed Miss Hall, you know. The dearest woman in the world, Miss Hall, and so pretty your breath went away. I had piano lessons with her, and when she played the piano, when she said hello and when she said good-bye—it was like my heart would stop." Her voice had taken on an impersonal tone, as though she were talking of matters belonging to another age, and in which she was not concerned directly. "It was the end of summer when she married him—September, I think. She went to Atlanta, and they were married there, and she never came back. It was just that sudden." She snapped her fingers. "Just like that. I saw a picture of him in the paper. Sometimes I think if she'd known how much I loved her— why are there some you can't ever tell?—I think maybe she wouldn't have married; maybe it would've all been different, like I wanted it." She turned her face into the pillow, and if she cried there was no sound.

On May twentieth she was eighteen; it seemed incredible—Vincent had thought her many years older. He wanted to introduce her at a surprise party, but had finally to admit that this was an unsuitable plan. First off, though the subject was always there on the tip of his tongue, not once had he ever mentioned D. J. to any of his friends; secondly, he could visualize discouragingly well the entertainment provided them at meeting a girl about whom, while they openly shared an apartment, he knew nothing, not even her name. Still the birthday called for some kind of treat. Dinner and the theater were hopeless. She hadn't, through no fault of his, a dress of any sort. He'd given her forty-odd dollars to buy clothes, and here is what she spent it on: a leather windbreaker, a set of military brushes, a raincoat, a cigarette lighter. Also, her suitcase, which she'd brought to the apartment, had contained nothing but hotel soap, a pair of scissors she used for pruning her hair, two Bibles, and an appalling color-tinted photograph. The photograph showed a simpering middle-aged woman with dumpy features. There was an inscription: Best Wishes and Good Luck from Martha Lovejoy Hall.

Because she could not cook they had their meals out; his salary and the limitations of her wardrobe confined them mostly to the Automat—her favorite: the macaroni was so delicious!—or one of the bar-grills along Third. And so the birthday dinner was eaten in the Automat. She'd scrubbed her face until the skin shone red, trimmed and shampooed her hair, and with the messy skill of a six-year-old playing grownup, varnished her nails. She wore the leather windbreaker, and on it pinned a sheaf of violets he'd given her; it must have looked amusing, for two rowdy girls sharing their table giggled frantically. Vincent said if they didn't shut up . . .

"Oh, yeah, who do you think you are?"

"Superman. Jerk thinks he's superman."

It was too much, and Vincent lost his temper. He shoved back from the table, upsetting a ketchup jar. "Let's get the hell out of here," he said, but D. J., who had paid the fracas no attention whatever, went right on spooning blackberry cobbler; furious as he was, he waited quietly until she finished, for he respected her remoteness, and yet wondered in what period of time she lived. It was futile, he'd discovered, to question her past; still, she seemed only now and then aware of the present, and it was likely the future didn't mean much to her. Her mind was like a mirror reflecting blue space in a barren room.

"What would you like now?" he said, as they came into the street. "We could ride in a cab through the park."

She wiped off with her jacket-cuff flecks of blackberry staining the corners of her mouth, and said, "I want to go to a picture show."

The movies. Again. In the last month he'd seen so many films, snatches of Hollywood dialogue rumbled in his dreams. On Saturday at her insistence they'd bought tickets to three different theaters, cheap places where smells of latrine disinfectant poisoned the air. And each morning before leaving for work he left on the mantel fifty cents—rain or shine, she went to a picture show. But Vincent was sensitive enough to see why: there had been in his own life a certain time of limbo when he'd gone to movies every day, often sitting through several repeats of the same film; it was in its way like religion, for there, watching the shifting patterns of black and white, he knew a release of conscience similar to the kind a man must find confessing to his father.

"Handcuffs," she said, referring to an incident in *The Thirty-Nine Steps*, which they'd seen at the Beverly in a program of Hitchcock revivals. "That blonde woman and the man handcuffed together—well, it made me think of something else." She stepped into a pair of his pajamas, pinned the corsage of violets to the edge of her pillow, and folded up on the bed. "People getting caught like that, locked together."

Vincent yawned. "Uh huh," he said, and turned off the lights. "Again, happy birthday darling, it was a happy birthday?"

She said, "Once I was in this place, and there were two girls dancing; they were so free—there was just them and nobody else, and it was beautiful like a sunset." She was silent a long while; then, her slow Southern voice dragging over the words: "It was mighty nice of you to bring me violets."

"Glad—like them," he answered sleepily.

"It's a shame they have to die."

"Yes, well, good night."

"Good night."

Close-up. Oh, but John, it isn't for my sake after all we've the children to consider a divorce would ruin their lives! Fadeout. The screen trembles; rattle of drums, flourish of trumpets: R.K.O. PRESENTS . . .

Here is a hall without exit, a tunnel without end. Overhead, chandeliers sparkle, and wind-bent candles float on currents of air. Before him is an old man rocking in a rocking chair, an old man with yellow-dyed hair, powdered cheeks, kewpie-doll lips: Vincent recognizes Vincent. Go away, screams Vincent, the young and handsome, but Vincent, the old and horrid, creeps forward on all fours, and climbs spiderlike onto his back. Threats, pleas, blows, nothing will dislodge him. And so he races with his shadow, his rider jogging up and down. A serpent of lightning blazes, and all at once the tunnel seethes with men wearing white tie and tails, women costumed in brocaded gowns. He is humiliated; how gauche they must think him appearing at so elegant a gathering carrying on his back, like Sinbad, a sordid old man. The guests stand about in petrified pairs, and there is no conversation. He notices then that many are also saddled with malevolent semblances of themselves, outward embodiments of inner decay. Just beside him a lizard-like man rides an albino-eyed Negro. A man is coming toward him, the host; short, florid, bald, he steps lightly, precisely in glacé shoes; one arm, held stiffly crooked, supports a massive headless hawk whose talons, latched to the wrist, draw blood. The hawk's wings unfurl as its master struts by. On a pedestal there is perched an old-time phonograph. Winding the handle, the host supplies a record: a tinny worn-out waltz vibrates the morning-glory horn. He lifts a hand, and in a soprano voice announces: "Attention! The dancing will commence." The host with his hawk weaves in and out as round and round they dip, they turn. The walls widen, the ceiling grows tall. A girl glides into Vincent's arms, and a cracked, cruel imitation of his voice says: "Lucille, how divine; that exquisite scent, is it violet?" This is Cousin Lucille, and then, as they circle the room, her face changes. Now he waltzes with another. "Why, Connie, Connie Silver! How marvelous to see you," shrieks the voice, for Connie is quite deaf. Suddenly a gentleman with a bullet-bashed head cuts in: "Gordon, forgive me, I never meant . . ." but they are gone, Gordon and Connie, dancing together. Again, a new partner. It is D. J., and she too has a figure barnacled to her back, an enchanting auburn-haired child; like an emblem of innocence, the child cuddles to her chest a snowball kitten. "I am heavier than I look," says the child, and the terrible voice retorts, "But I am heaviest of all." The instant their hands meet he begins to feel the weight upon him diminish; the old Vincent is fading. His feet lift off the floor, he floats upward from her embrace. The victrola grinds away loud as ever, but he is rising high, and the white receding faces gleam below like mushrooms on a dark meadow.

The host releases his hawk, sends it soaring. Vincent thinks, no matter, it is a blind thing, and the wicked are safe among the blind. But the hawk wheels above him, swoops down, claws foremost; at last he knows there is to be no freedom.

And the blackness of the room filled his eyes. One arm lolled over the bed's edge, his pillow had fallen to the floor. Instinctively he reached out, asking mother-comfort of the girl beside him. Sheets smooth and cold; emptiness, and the tawdry fragrance of drying violets. He snapped up straight: "You, where are you?"

The French doors were open. An ashy trace of moon swayed on the threshold, for it was not yet light, and in the kitchen the refrigerator purred like a giant cat. A stack of papers rustled on the desk. Vincent called again, softly this time, as if he wished himself unheard. Rising, he stumbled forward on dizzy legs, and looked into the yard. She was there, leaning, half-kneeling, against the heaven tree. "What?" and she whirled around. He could not see her well, only a dark substantial shape. She came closer. A finger pressed her lips.

"What is it?" he whispered.

She rose on tiptoe, and her breath tingled in his ear. "I warn you, go inside."

"Stop this foolishness," he said in a normal voice. "Out here barefooted, you'll catch . . ." but she clamped a hand over his mouth.

"I saw him," she whispered. "He's here."

Vincent knocked her hand away. It was hard not to slap her. "Him! Him! Him! What's the matter with you? Are you—" he tried too late to prevent the word—"crazy?" There, the acknowledgment of something he'd known, but had not allowed his conscious mind to crystallize. And he thought: Why should this make a difference? A man cannot be held to account for those he loves. Untrue. Feeble-witted Lucille weaving mosaics on silk, embroidering his name on scarves; Connie, in her hushed deaf world, listening for his footstep, a sound she would surely hear; Allen T. Baker thumbing his photograph, still needing love, but old now, and lost—all betrayed. And he'd betrayed himself with talents unexploited, voyages never taken, promises unfulfilled. There had seemed nothing left for him until—oh, why in his lovers must he always find the broken image of himself? Now, as he looked at her in the aging dawn, his heart was cold with the death of love.

She moved away, and under the tree. "Leave me here," she said, her eyes scanning tenement windows. "Only a moment."

Vincent waited, waited. On all sides windows looked down like the doors of dreams, and overhead, four flights up, a family's laundry whipped a washline. The setting moon was like the early moon of dusk, a vaporish cartwheel, and the sky, draining of dark, was washed with gray. Sunrise wind shook the leaves of the heaven tree, and in the paling light the yard assumed a pattern, objects a position, and from the roofs came the throaty morning rumble of pigeons. A light went on. Another.

And at last she lowered her head; whatever she was looking for, she had not found it. Or, he wondered as she turned to him with tilted lips, had she?

"Well, you're home kinda early, aren't you, Mr. Waters?" It was Mrs. Brennan, the super's bowlegged wife. "And, well, Mr. Waters—lovely weather, ain't it?—you and me got sumpin' to talk about."

"Mrs. Brennan—" how hard it was to breathe, to speak; the words grated his hurting throat, sounded loud as thunderclaps—"I'm rather ill, so if you don't mind . . ." and he tried to brush past her.

"Say, that's a pity. Ptomaine, must be ptomaine. Yessir, I tell you a person can't be too careful. It's them Jews, you know. They run all them delicatessens. Uh uh, none of that Jew food for me." She stepped before the gate, blocking his path, and pointed an admonishing finger: "Trouble with you, Mr. Waters, is that you don't lead no kinda *normal* life."

A knot of pain was set like a malignant jewel in the core of his head; each aching motion made jeweled pinpoints of color flare out. The super's wife blabbed on, but there were blank moments when, fortunately, he could not hear at all. It was like a radio—the volume turned low, then full blast. "Now I know she's a decent Christian lady, Mr. Waters, or else what would a gentleman like you be doing with—hm. Still, the fact is, Mr. Cooper don't tell lies, and he's a real calm man, besides. Been gas meter man for this district I don't know how long." A truck rolled down the street spraying water, and her voice, submerged below its roar, came up again like a shark. "Mr. Cooper had every reason to believe she meant to kill him—well, you can imagine, her standin' there with them scissors, and shoutin'. She called him an Eyetalian name. Now all you got to do is look at Mr. Cooper to know he ain't no Eyetalian. Well, you can see, Mr. Waters, such carryings-on are bound to give the house a bad . . ."

Brittle sunshine plundering the depths of his eyes made tears, and the super's wife, wagging her fingers, seemed to break into separate pieces: a nose, a chin, a red, red eye. "Mr. Destronelli," he said. "Excuse me, Mrs. Brennan, I mean excuse me." She thinks I'm drunk, and I'm sick, and can't she see I'm sick? "My guest is leaving. She's leaving today, and she won't be back."

"Well, now, you don't say," said Mrs. Brennan, clucking her tongue. "Looks like she needs a rest, poor little thing. So pale, sorta. Course I don't want no more to do with them Eyetalians than the next one, but imagine thinking Mr. Cooper was an Eyetalian. Why, he's white as you or me." She tapped his shoulder solicitously. "Sorry you feel so sick, Mr. Waters; ptomaine, I tell you. A person can't be too care . . .''

The hall smelled of cooking and incinerator ashes. There was a stairway which he never used, his apartment being on the first floor, straight ahead. A match snapped fire, and Vincent, groping his way, saw a small boy— he was not more than three or four—squatting under the stairwell; he was playing with a big box of kitchen matches, and Vincent's presence appeared not to interest him. He simply struck another match. Vincent could not make his mind work well enough to phrase a reprimand, and as he waited there, tongue-tied, a door, his door, opened.

Hide. For if she saw him she would know something was wrong, suspect something. And if she spoke, if their eyes met, then he would never be able to go through with it. So he pressed into a dark corner behind the little boy, and the little boy said, "Whatcha doin', Mister?" She was coming —he heard the slap of her sandals, the green whisper of her raincoat. "Whatcha doin', Mister?" Quickly, his heart banging in his chest, Vincent stooped and, squeezing the child against him, pressed his hand over its mouth so it could not make a sound. He did not see her pass; it was later, after the front door clicked, that he realized she was gone. The little boy sank back on the floor. "Whatcha doin', Mister?"

Four aspirins, one right after the other, and he came back into the room; the bed had not been tidied for a week, a spilt ash tray messed the floor, odds and ends of clothing decorated improbable places, lampshades and such. But tomorrow, if he felt better, there would be a general cleaning; perhaps he'd have the walls repainted, maybe fix up the yard. Tomorrow he could begin thinking about his friends again, accept invitations, entertain. And yet this prospect, tasted in advance, was without flavor: all he'd known before seemed to him now sterile and spurious. Footsteps in the hall; could she return this soon, the movie over, the afternoon gone? Fever can make time pass so queerly, and for an instant he felt as though his bones were floating loose inside him. Clopclop, a child's sloppy shoefall, the footsteps passed up the stairs, and Vincent moved, floated toward the mirrored closet. He longed to hurry, knowing he must, but the air seemed thick with gummy fluid. He brought her suitcase from the closet, and put it on the bed, a sad cheap suitcase with rusty locks and a warped hide. He eyed it with guilt. Where would she go? How would she live? When he'd broken with Connie, Gordon, all the others, there had been about it at least a certain dignity. Really, though—and he'd thought it out—there was no other way. So he gathered her belongings. Miss Martha Lovejoy Hall peeked out from under the leather windbreaker, her music-teacher's face smiling an oblique reproach. Vincent turned her over, face down, and tucked in the frame an envelope containing twenty dollars. That would buy a ticket back to Glass Hill, or wherever it was she came from. Now he tried to close the case, and, too weak with fever, collapsed on the bed. Quick yellow wings glided through the window. A butterfly. He'd never seen a butterfly in this city, and it was like a floating mysterious flower, like a sign of some sort, and he watched with a kind of horror as it waltzed in the air. Outside, somewhere, the razzle-dazzle of a beggar's grind-organ started up; it sounded like a broken-down pianola, and it played *La Marseillaise*. The butterfly lighted on her painting, crept across crystal eyes, and flattened its wings like a ribbon bow over the loose head. He fished about in the suitcase until he found her scissors. He first purposed to slash the butterfly's wings, but it spiraled to the ceiling and hung there like a star. The scissors stabbed the hawk's heart, ate through canvas like a ravening steel mouth, scraps of picture flaking the floor like cuttings of stiff hair. He went on his knees, pushed the pieces into a pile, put them in the suitcase, and slammed the lid shut. He was crying. And through the tears the butterfly magnified on the ceiling, huge as a bird, and there was more: a flock of lilting, winking yellow; whispering lonesomely, like surf sucking a shore. The wind from their wings blew the room into space. He heaved forward, the suitcase banging his leg, and threw open the door. A match flared. The little boy said: "Whatcha doin', Mister?" And Vincent, setting the suitcase in the hall, grinned sheepishly. He closed the door like a thief, bolted the safety lock and, pulling up a chair, tilted it under the knob. In the still room there was only the subtlety of shifting sunlight and a crawling butterfly; it drifted downward like a tricky scrap of crayon paper, and landed on a candlestick. *Sometimes he is not a man at all*—she'd told him that, huddling here on the bed, talking swiftly in the minutes before dawn—*sometimes he is something very different: a hawk, a child, a butterfly.* And then she'd said: *At the place where they took me there were hundreds of old ladies, and young men, and one of the young men said he was a pirate, and one of the old ladies—she was near ninety—used to make me feel her stomach. "Feel," she'd say, "feel how strong he kicks?" This old lady took painting class, too, and her paintings looked like crazy quilts. And naturally he was in this place. Mr. Destronelli. Only he called himself Gum. Doctor Gum. Oh, he didn't fool me, even though he wore a gray wig, and made himself up to look real old and kind, I knew. And then one day I left, ran clear away, and hid under a lilac bush, and a man came along in a little red car, and he had a little mouse-haired mustache, and little cruel eyes. But it was him. And when I told him who he was he made me get out of his car. And then another man, that was in Philadelphia, picked me up in a café and took me into an alley. He talked Italian, and had tattoo pictures all over. But it was him.*

*And the next man, he was the one who painted his toenails, sat down beside
me in a movie because he thought I was a boy, and when he found out I
wasn't he didn't get mad but let me live in his room, and cooked pretty things
for me to eat. But he wore a silver locket and one day I looked inside and
there was a picture of Miss Hall. So I knew it was him, so I had this feeling
she was dead, so I knew he was going to murder me. And he will. He will.*"
Dusk, and nightfall, and the fibers of sound called silence wove a shiny blue
mask. Waking, he peered through eyeslits, heard the frenzied pulse-beat of
his watch, the scratch of a key in a lock. Somewhere in this dusk a murderer
separates himself from shadow and with a rope follows the flash of silk legs
up doomed stairs. And here the dreamer staring through his mask dreams of
deceit. Without investigating he knows the suitcase is missing, that she has
come, that she has gone; why, then, does he feel so little the pleasure of
safety, and only cheated, and small—small as the night when he searched
the moon through an old man's telescope?

III

Like fragments of an old letter, scattered popcorn lay trampled flat, and
she, leaning back in a watchman's attitude, allowed her gaze to hunt among
it, as if deciphering here and there a word, an answer. Her eyes shifted dis-
creetly to the man mounting the steps, Vincent. There was about him the
freshness of a shower, shave, cologne, but dreary blue circled his eyes, and
the crisp seersucker into which he'd changed had been made for a heavier
man: a long month of pneumonia, and wakeful burning nights had lightened
his weight a dozen pounds, and more. Each morning, evening, meeting her
here at his gate, or near the gallery, or outside the restaurant where he
lunched, a nameless disorder took hold, a paralysis of time and identity. The
wordless pantomime of her pursuit contracted his heart, and there were
coma-like days when she seemed not one, but all a multiple person, and her
shadow in the street every shadow, following and followed. And once they'd
been alone together in an automatic elevator, and he'd screamed: "I am not
him! Only me, only me!" But she smiled as she'd smiled telling of the man
with painted toenails, because, after all, she knew.

It was suppertime, and, not knowing where to eat, he paused under a
street lamp that, blooming abruptly, fanned complex light over stone; while
he waited there came a clap of thunder, and all along the street every face but
two, his and the girl's, tilted upwards. A blast of river breeze tossed the children's laughter as they, linking arms, pranced like carousel ponies, and carried the mama's voice who, leaning from a window, howled: rain, Rachel,
rain—gonna rain gonna rain! And the gladiola, ivy-filled flower cart jerked
crazily as the peddler, one eye slanted skyward, raced for shelter. A potted

geranium fell off, and the little girls gathered the blooms and tucked them behind their ears. The blending spatter of running feet and raindrops tinkled on the xylophone sidewalks—the slamming of doors, the lowering of windows, then nothing but silence, and rain. Presently, with slow scraping steps, she came below the lamp to stand beside him, and it was as if the sky were a thunder-cracked mirror, for the rain fell between them like a curtain of splintered glass.

Questions for Discussion

1. To what extent does D. J. reflect the dilemma of Vincent?

2. What is meant by the statement that Vincent "substituted for a sense of reality a knowledge of time, and place"?

3. Explain the significance of D. J's painting for Vincent? Why does he destroy it?

4. What do all the people Vincent loved in the past have in common? How are they similar to himself as well as to D. J.?

5. At the end of his dream Vincent "knows there is to be no freedom." What does this mean in terms of the whole story?

6. What is D. J's relation to the Mr. Destronelli? How does she associate him with Vincent?

7. How might Vincent be compared with William Wilson? What do the mirror images at the end of "William Wilson" and "The Headless Hawk" have in common?

8. Explain the reason for including in the story the tart, realistic language of the city such as "Ain't but a nickel, bub."

9. What is the connection between the quotation from Job and the story? Note the emphasis on darkness and blindness in the story.

Biographical Notes

Geoffrey Chaucer (*ca.* 1343-1400) was born in London, the son of a wealthy middle-class wine merchant. He spent most of his life in aristocratic and court circles and held a number of positions including that of a page in one of the great households of England, a soldier in France, an envoy for the King in Italy and France, Controller of the Customs at the port of London, Justice of the Peace for Kent, and Clerk of the King's Works. Such a variety of experiences brought him in contact with continental literature and enabled him to write on all aspects of English society in both high and low styles. His two most important works are *Troilus and Criseyde* (1385) and *The Canterbury Tales*, which he worked on during the last fourteen years of his life.

William Shakespeare (1564-1616) was born in Stratford-on-Avon and educated in the Stratford Grammar School. Probably by 1588 he was in London as an actor, and by 1594 he was a member of the Lord Chamberlain's Men (later the King's Men), the most successful company of the day. He was the principal playwright for this group, who performed in their own Globe Theater for many years. By the time he wrote *King Lear*, about 1605, he had had a long experience in writing poetic drama. After the period of his great tragedies he wrote his final series of plays, which culminated in *The Tempest* (1611). Earlier he had composed a remarkable sequence of 154 sonnets—remarkable because of their variations on the traditional Petrarchan themes. They were published in 1609.

Samuel Taylor Coleridge (1772-1834) was born in rural Devonshire and educated in London and at Cambridge; he did not take a degree. In 1795 he met Wordsworth, and the two poets formed a friendship and collaboration which culminated in their joint publication of *Lyrical Ballads* in 1798. "The Rime of the Ancient Mariner" is Coleridge's chief work in that volume. Shortly thereafter Coleridge and the Wordsworths went to Germany, where he began his lifelong study of the German philosophers and critics. Coleridge's poetry rapidly declined in power, but he remained an important man of letters in London.

John Keats (1795-1821) was born in London. His father was head ostler at a livery stable, but the boy was sent to a good private school, where he was fortunate enough to be encouraged in his literary pursuits. Later he met the critic Leigh Hunt, who introduced him to several important writers, including Shelley. His first book, *Poems*, was published in 1817. His remaining years, however, were often filled with disappointments despite the brilliant poetry which he was writing. His emotional life was intense, probably because he knew that his life would be cut short. He died of tuberculosis in Rome.

Alfred, Lord Tennyson (1809-1892) was the son of a clergyman of the Church of England and was educated at Cambridge. He was already publishing poems when he was a student, and by 1830 he brought out *Poems Chiefly Lyrical*. More important was the *Poems* of 1842. In 1850 he published his long elegiac poem *In Memoriam* and he became poet laureate, succeeding Wordsworth. During the remainder of his long life he was a very influential poet with a large public, and eventually he was elevated to the peerage.

Alexander Pushkin (1799-1837) was born in Moscow of a noble family. His literary interests were encouraged by his father. He attended a lyceum which had been established by the czar for the sons of the nobility, and after his graduation he was attached to the Foreign Office at St. Petersburg. Later he was a civil servant. After 1820, when he published *Ruslan and Ludmila*, a long narrative poem, he was almost a national poet. His subsequent work in poetry includes his play, *Boris Godunov* (1825), and his masterpiece, *Eugene Onegin* (finished in 1831). His prose fiction came later, and it includes *The Queen of Spades* (1834) and *The Captain's Daughter* (1836), his only full-length novel. He was killed in a duel.

Edgar Allan Poe (1809-1849) was born in Boston as the child of poor actors. His mother died on tour in Richmond, Virginia, in 1811, and the infant became the ward of John Allan, a rich tobacco merchant. He spent a brief period at the University of Virginia, but his gambling debts were ruinous. He subsequently failed in a military career. Meanwhile he published a small volume, *Tamerlane and Other Poems*, in 1827, and after 1830 he had to make his living by writing. He published large numbers of stories and critical essays in magazines, several of which he edited. He was one of the first writers to make high claims for the short story as a form—rating it above the full-length novel.

Gustave Flaubert (1821-1880) was born in Rouen, France. Aside from a trip to the Near East and periods of residence in Paris, he spent most of his life in the village of Croisset near Rouen. His first and most famous novel, *Madame Bovary*, appeared in 1859 and created a scandal. His other novels are *Salammbo* (1862), *The Sentimental Education* (1869), *The Temptation of Saint Anthony* (1874), and the unfinished *Bouvard and Pecuchet*. "St. Julian the Hospitaller" is one of the *Three Stories* (1877), his last book.

Franz Kafka (1883-1924) was born into a rich jewish family in Prague. He was educated in law, though his chief interest was already literature. For a few years he worked in an insurance office; then he went to the front in World War I and his health was virtually destroyed. Most of his work was published posthumously and against his wishes. "The Hunter Gracchus" is drawn from his book of stories, *The Great Wall of China*. His other works include the novels *The Trial, The Castle,* and *America*.

Walter de la Mare (1873-1956) was born in Kent, England, and educated at St. Paul's Cathedral Choir School. He spent eighteen years in the Standard Oil Company before devoting himself altogether to the literary arts. He wrote short stories and novels as well as verse. His two principal volumes were *Collected Poems* (1942) and *Collected Rhymes and Verses* (1944). In his late years he wrote two long poems, *The Traveller* (1946) and *Winged Chariot* (1951).

Robert Frost (1874-1963) was born in San Francisco. His parents were New Englanders, and when his father died, his mother took him back to Massachusetts. He attended Dartmouth and Harvard for short periods, but he did not take a degree. Although he was serious about writing verse, he had to earn his living at farming and school-teaching for many years. In 1912 he sold his farm and took his family to England, where he found congenial literary friends like Edward Thomas. Here his first book, *A Boy's Will*, was published in 1913. It was followed in 1914 by *North of Boston*. Both books were soon reprinted in the United States and Frost returned. His later books are too numerous to mention here; most of them are included in *Complete Poems* (1949).

Elizabeth Bowen (1899-) was born in Ireland and educated in England. She has divided her life between those two countries, but for many years she has lived in her ancestral home, Bowen's Court, County Cork, Ireland. Her collections of short stories include *Joining Charles* (1929), *Look at All Those Roses* (1941), and *Ivy Grips the Steps* (1946), from which "The Demon Lover" is taken. Her best-known novels are *The Death of the Heart* (1939) and *The Heat of the Day* (1949).

Truman Capote (1924-) was born in New Orleans and educated at various schools in New York City and Connecticut. He has been a quite successful writer since the publication of his novel *Other Voices, Other Rooms* in 1948. His other books include a collection of stories, *The Tree of Night* (1949); a short novel, *Breakfast at Tiffany's* (1958); and a "non-fiction novel," *In Cold Blood* (1966).